THE POLKA DOT DOOR

by Polkaroo

ACTIVITY BOOK

with Catherine Ripley

Stoddart

A Somerville House Book

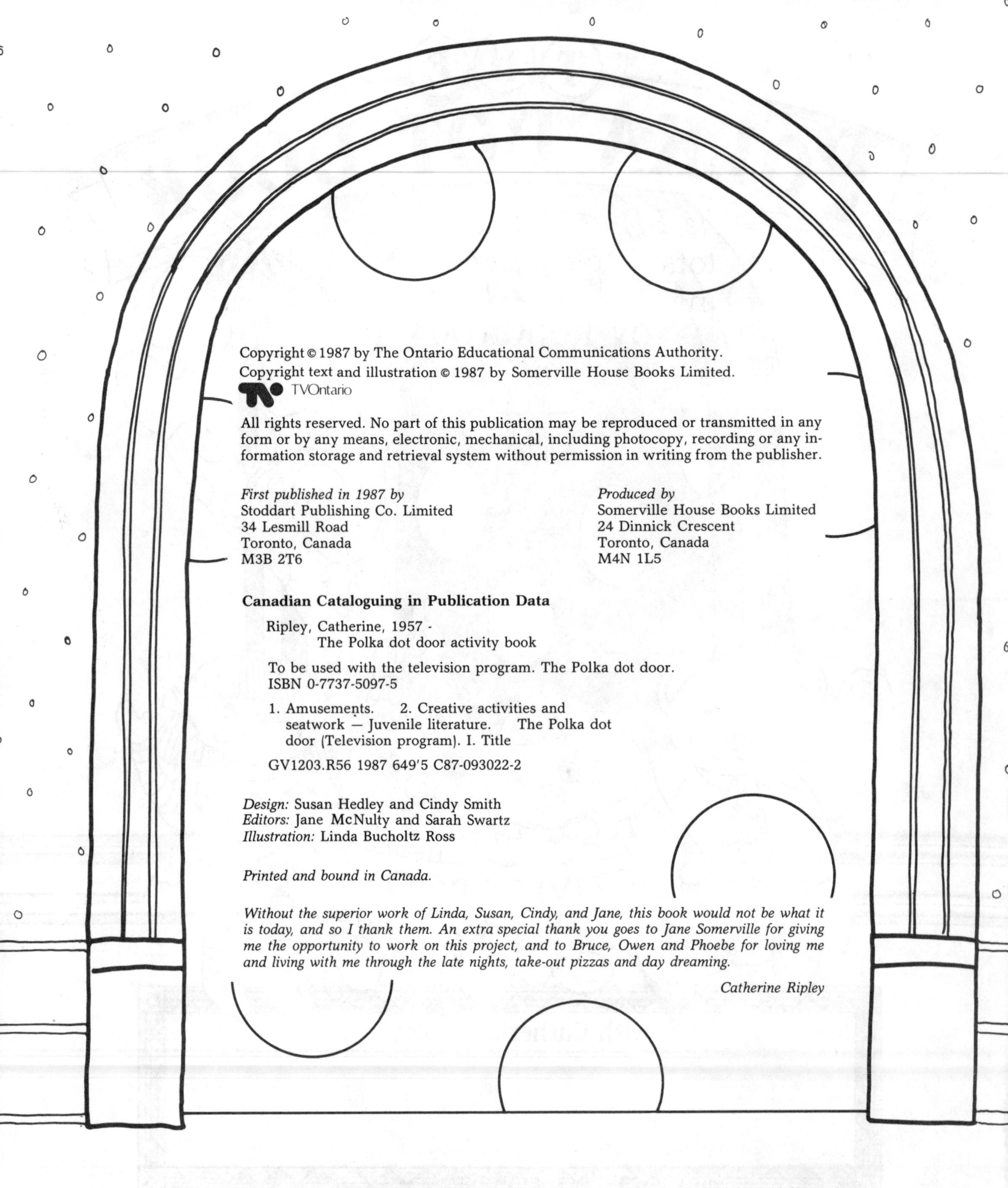

TVOntario

First published in 1987 by
Stoddart Publishing Co. Limited
34 Lesmill Road
Toronto, Canada
M3B 2T6

Produced by
Somerville House Books Limited
24 Dinnick Crescent
Toronto, Canada
M4N 1L5

Canadian Cataloguing in Publication Data

Ripley, Catherine, 1957 -
The Polka dot door activity book

To be used with the television program. The Polka dot door.
ISBN 0-7737-5097-5

1. Amusements. 2. Creative activities and seatwork — Juvenile literature. The Polka dot door (Television program). I. Title

GV1203.R56 1987 649'5 C87-093022-2

Design: Susan Hedley and Cindy Smith
Editors: Jane McNulty and Sarah Swartz
Illustration: Linda Bucholtz Ross

Printed and bound in Canada.

Without the superior work of Linda, Susan, Cindy, and Jane, this book would not be what it is today, and so I thank them. An extra special thank you goes to Jane Somerville for giving me the opportunity to work on this project, and to Bruce, Owen and Phoebe for loving me and living with me through the late nights, take-out pizzas and day dreaming.

Catherine Ripley

The Polka Dot Door Activity Book

Welcome to *The Polka Dot Door Activity Book*. There's lots to do, read and make. Have fun!

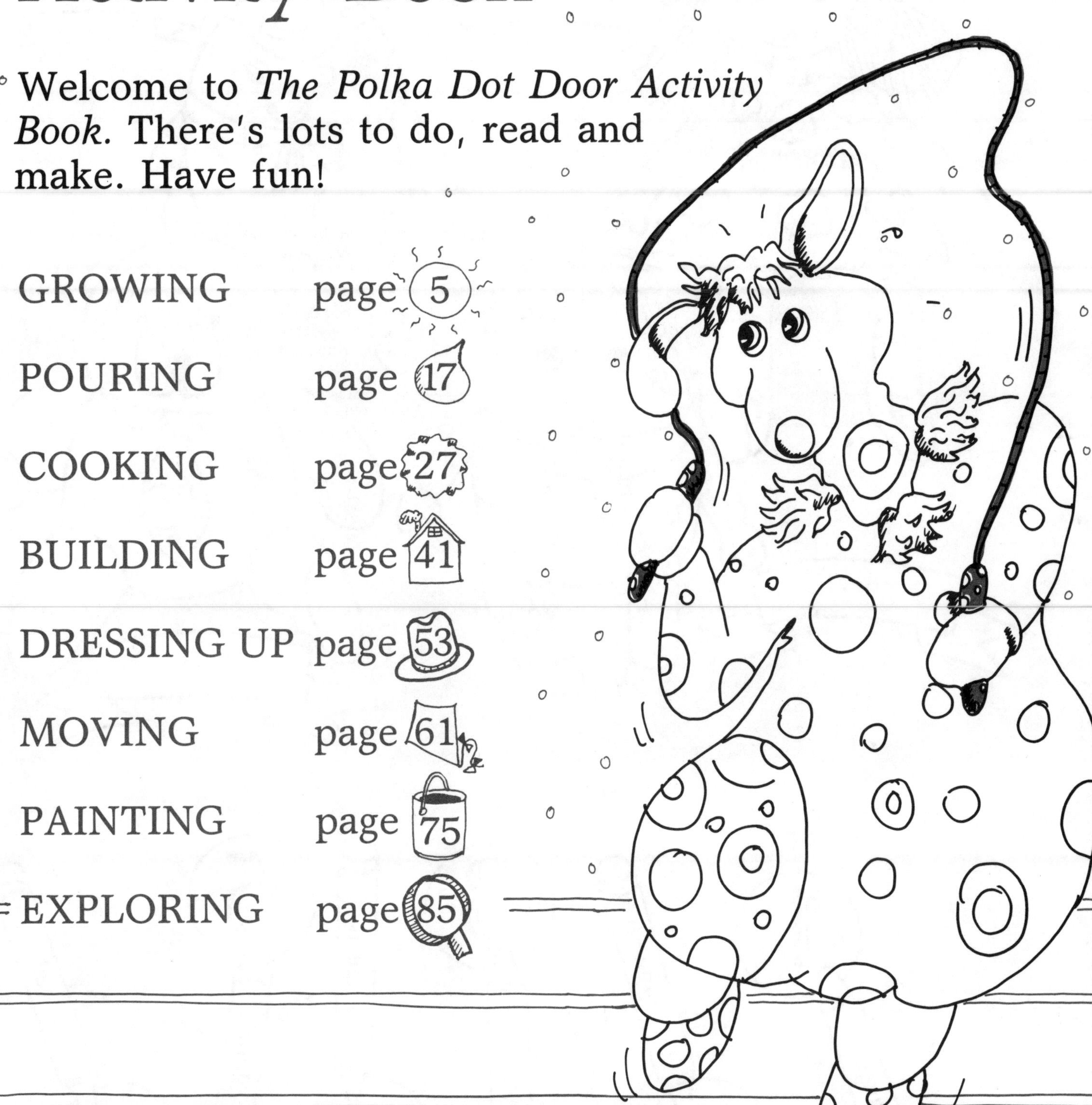

This is a safety symbol. If you see this symbol, be extra careful and ask for a grownup's help.

Color Polkaroo's Friends

Marigold

Dumpty

Humpty

Bear

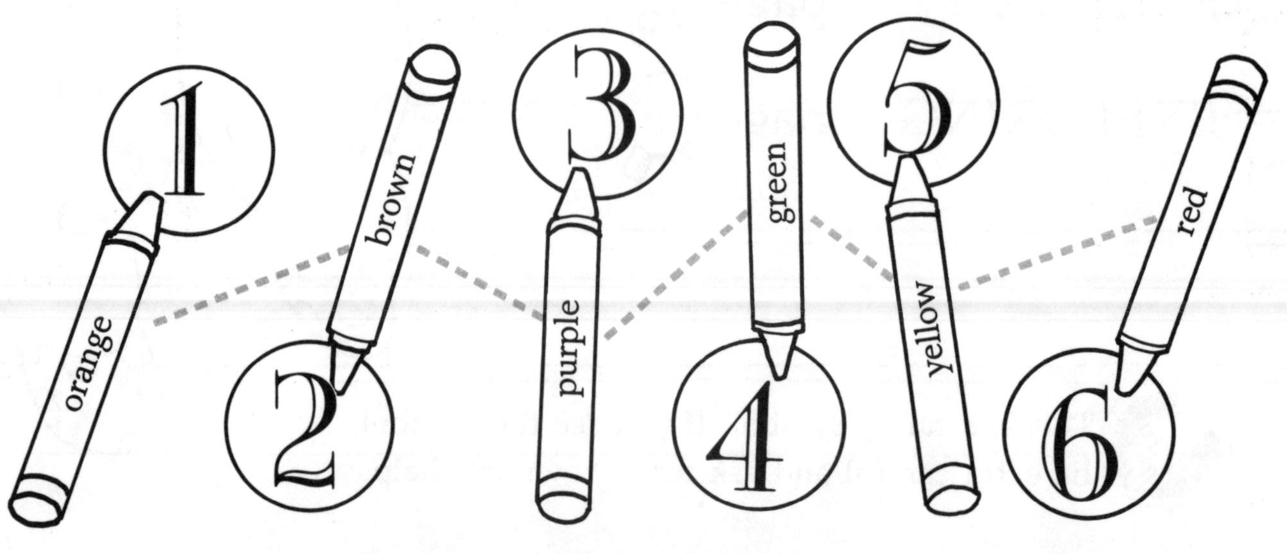

GROWING

6 What Grows?

Look carefully at the things that each toy has. Circle the things that grow and draw an "X" through the things that don't. Who has the most things that grow?

What Doesn't?

Answer: The french fries, pop can, sand and bucket, Polkaroo doll, pillow and cookies don't grow. All the others do. Marigold has the most things that grow.

Watch It Grow!

Turn kitchen leftovers into green growing things.

Carrot Tops

You need: two or three carrot tops, a shallow dish, water.

- Ask a grownup to save you some sliced-off carrot tops.
- Place the tops in a shallow dish.
- Keep the tops watered. In a few days, see them send up tiny new shoots.
- Try beet tops, too!

Avocado Bottom

You need: three toothpicks, an avocado pit, a glass or jar, water.

- Ask a grownup to help you stick three toothpicks into an avocado pit.
- Suspend the pit in a glass or a jar. (See the picture.)
- Make sure the bottom of the pit is always in the water. Soon it will send out some roots.
- If you like, you can plant the pit gently in some soil in a pot when it has lots of roots.

Sponge Surprise

You need: a sponge, scissors, a waterproof container (milk carton, yogurt container or dishwashing liquid bottle), decorating items, grass seed, water.

- Ask a grownup to help you cut a sponge to fit the top of a waterproof container.
- Decorate the container with a funny face or pretty pattern.
- Wet the sponge, squeeze out the water and stuff it into the container until just the top shows.
- Sprinkle grass seed on top of the sponge.
- Water the sponge if it gets dry and watch for a head of hair to sprout!

10 Growing Isn't Always Up

by Emily Hearn

Growing isn't always up.
It's out,
It's in,
It's round and round.
Up to the sky,
Down in the ground.
You never know it's happening,
It doesn't make a sound,
You can't tell any difference
Until your toes feel scrunched,
And your T-shirt's bunched,
And your hat's too small —
Nothing seems to fit at all!

Inch by Inch

You need: ten long business envelopes, decorating items, a ruler, masking tape.

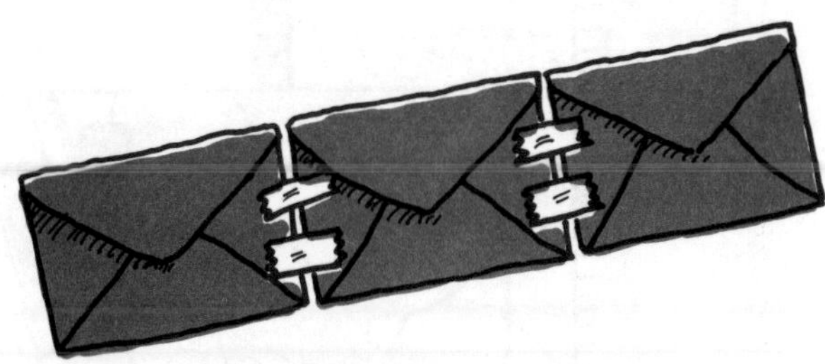

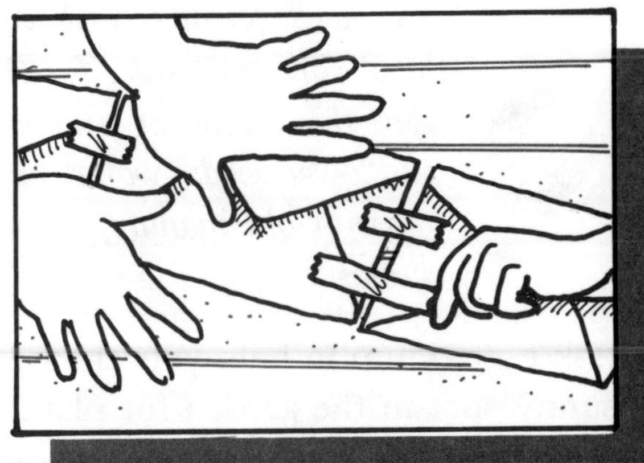

- Make a measuring chart to see how much you, your friends and your family grow in six months.
- Tape the envelopes end to end.
- Lay the envelope strip on the floor and decorate it with paints, crayons or markers.

- Ask a grownup to help you use a ruler to measure out and mark the inches (centimeters) along one side of the strip.

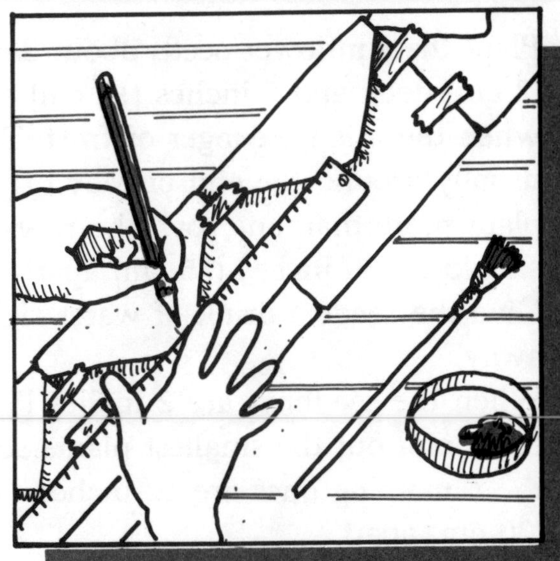

- Use masking tape to stick your chart to a door or wall.
- Stand against the tape and get someone to mark your height. Print your name and the date beside your height.
- Now measure your family and friends against the chart. Print their names and heights in different colors.
- Measure everyone again in six months. Who has grown? Has anybody shrunk?

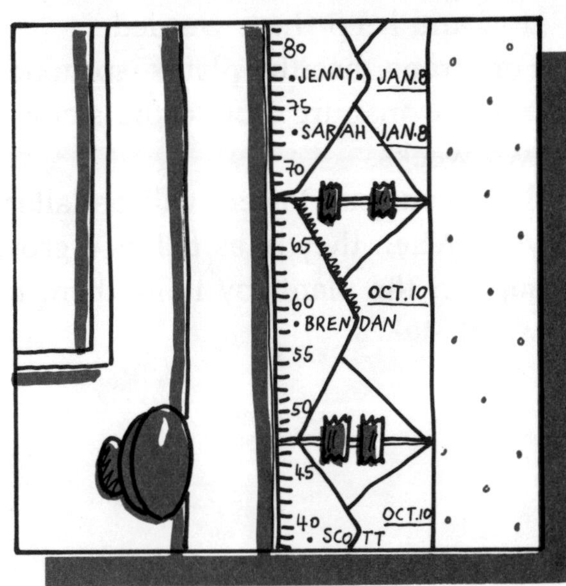

12 Super Sunflowers

You need: fertilizer (ask your local gardening store for the type that's best for your soil), sunflower seeds, water, peat moss or old manure, wood stakes.

- Ask a grownup to help you choose a sunny spot in the garden for planting in the spring, and mix fertilizer into the soil.
- Plant the sunflower seeds about 3/4 inch (2 cm) deep and 6 inches (15 cm) apart when there is no danger of frost. (This is usually around the end of May.) If you plant more than one row, the rows should be 30 inches (75 cm) apart.
- Give the seeds a drink of water right away.
- When the seedlings are 2 inches (5 cm) high, pull out the smallest plants so that the remaining ones are 12 inches (30 cm) apart.
- Water the plants whenever the soil is dry, and keep them weeded.
- For strong, healthy plants, sprinkle peat moss or manure around the stems every two weeks.
- Soon your sunflowers will be taller than you! When they're as tall as a grownup, support the plants by tying them to wood stakes.

Find Two the Same

Can you find two sunflowers that are exactly alike?

Answer: 1 and 5.

Apartment Dwellers

You can grow sunflowers, too. Put gravel in the bottom of a pot that has drainage holes. Add soil and plant three or four seeds. After they have sprouted, choose only one plant to keep. When its roots start crawling out the drainage holes, move the plant to an even bigger pot. Try not to disturb the roots too much. Keep as much soil around them as possible, and water the plant immediately after repotting.

14 Snazzy Snaps

You need: photos, jar lids, scissors, glue (white glue works best).

- Ask your parents for some photos of you when you were younger. Ask if you can cut these pictures.
- Collect some jar lids. (A baby-food jar lid would work well for a baby picture.)
- Ask a grownup to help you cut your pictures to fit the lids.
- Glue the photos into the jar lids. If the picture is smaller than the lid, first cut a circle of construction paper to fit the lid.
- If you like, you can glue your "framed" photos onto a strip of decorated cardboard.
- To hang your pictures on the wall, glue or tape a loop of ribbon or string onto the back of the lids or the cardboard.

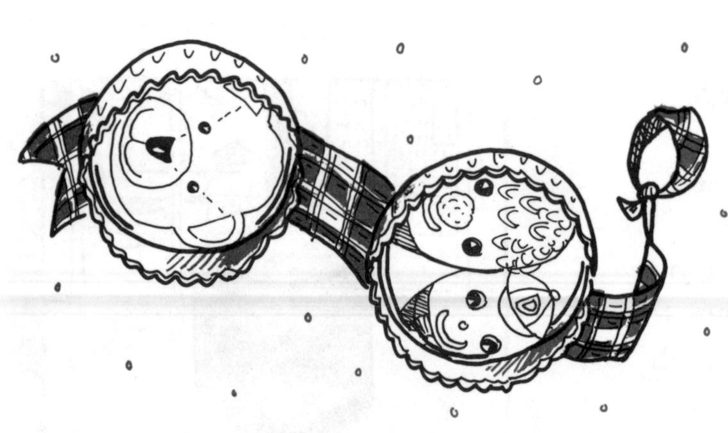

Flower Pot Picture

You need: construction paper, glue or tape, a paper cup, earth, candies or playdough, a stick (popsicle stick or sturdy tree twig).

- To make a gift for someone special, paste your picture into a jar lid as described in "Snazzy Snaps."
- Cut large petals out of brightly colored construction paper.
- Glue or tape these petals to the back of the lid.
- Tape a stick securely to the lid.
- Glue a circle of pretty paper to the back of the lid to cover up the stick, tape and petal ends.
- Stick your "flower" into a decorated paper cup filled with earth, candies or playdough.

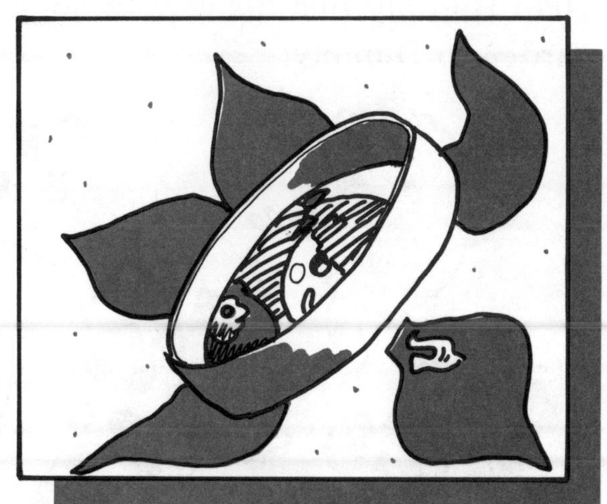

Help Humpty

Help Humpty find his way through the garden to Dumpty.

POURING

Rainy Rhymes

Rhyme with Rain

Circle the things that rhyme with "rain."
Can you think of any others?

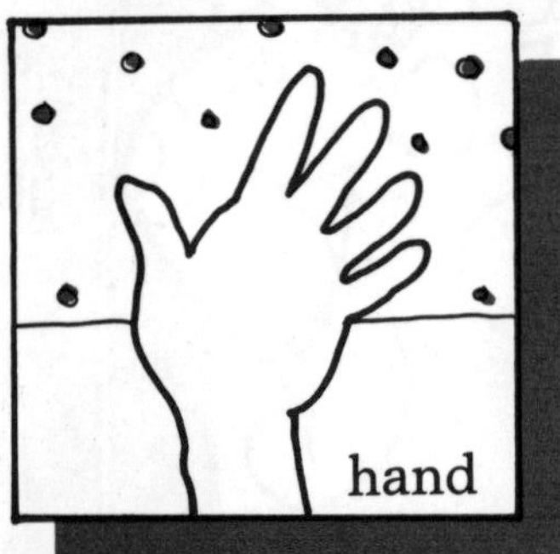

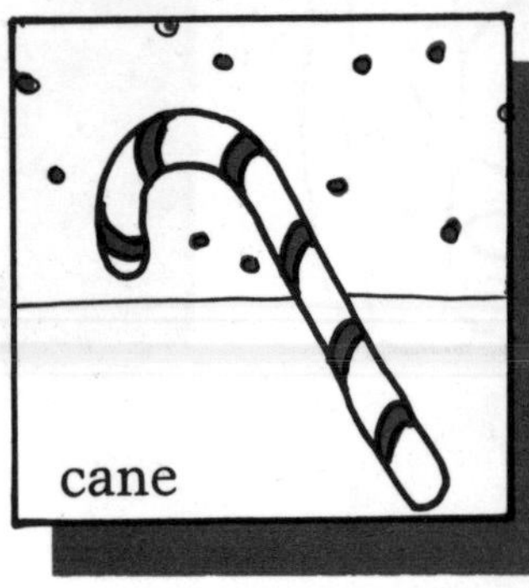

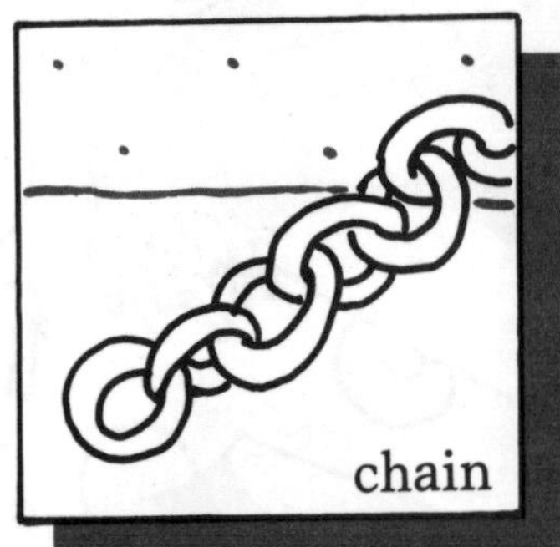

Rain, rain, go away
And come again
another day!

Answer: Hand, cake and pail don't rhyme with rain.

April showers bring May flowers!
Doctor Foster went to Gloucester,
In a shower of rain;
He stepped in a puddle
Right up to his middle,
And never went there again.

20 Make Bottle Music

You need: nine empty bottles (25-ounce [750 mL] pop bottles work well), water, labels, spoons.

- Ask a grownup to help you fill the first bottle with 1 inch (2.5 cm) of water and place it on your left.

- Fill the second bottle with 2 inches (5 cm) of water, the third with 3 inches (7.5 cm), and so on. Arrange the bottles in a row.

- Fill the ninth bottle right to the top.
- Tap the bottles gently with a wooden spoon. Do the notes sound all right?
- Depending on the type of bottle, you may have to adjust the water levels until the notes make a pleasing sound.
- Label the bottles from 1 to 9 as shown in the picture. Now turn the page to find some music to play on your bottles.

22 Bottle Tapping Tips

- Start off by using a wooden spoon. Hit the bottles lightly and quickly with the edge of the spoon.
- Try other types of spoons for different sound effects.

Note Guide

Hit the bottle as fast as you can.	= fast beat
Hit the bottle regularly.	= regular beat
Hit the bottle and hold the spoon there for a little longer than normal.	= slow beat

- Go through the tunes slowly. Bring forward only the bottles you need for each song. The theme song from "The Polka Dot Door" is the only one for which you need all nine bottles.
- First practice tapping the bottles in the proper order. When you can tap them well, try singing the words, too. Adjust the speed of your tapping to your singing.
- When you can play the tunes smoothly, ask your family or friends to sing along.
- Can you make up your own songs?

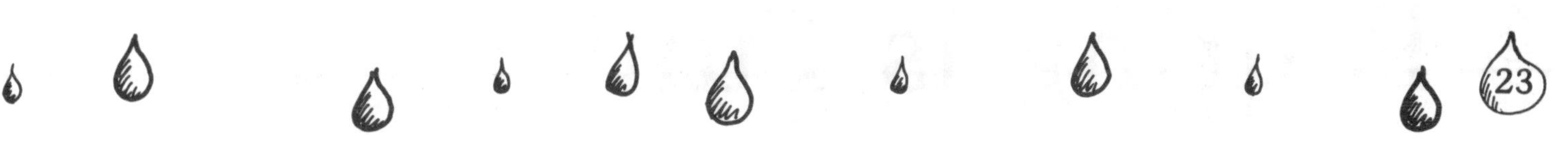

Ring Around the Roses

2	2	4	1	2	2
Ring	a-	round	the	ro-	ses,

2	2	4	1	2	4
Poc-	ket	full	of	po-	sies,

1	2	1	2	1	2	6	6
Hush	-a,	hush	-a,	we	all	fall	down!

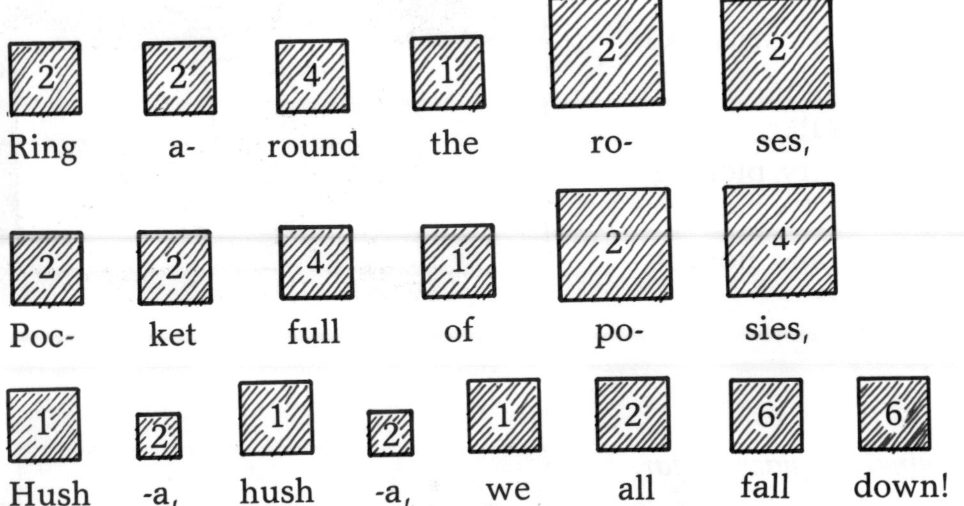

The Polka Dot Door (*Refrain*) *by Pat Patterson and Dodi Robb*

5	7	6	5	9
The	Pol-	ka	Dot	Door.

2	3	2	1	5
The	Pol -	ka	Dot	Door.

4	2	5	7	6	5	6	8
Let's	peep	through	the	Pol-	ka	Dot	Door.

9	9	8	7	9	6	4	2
Songs	and	sto-	ries	and	so	much	more!

5	5	1	1	3	5
Through	the	Pol-	ka	Dot	Door.

Pouring is Fun!

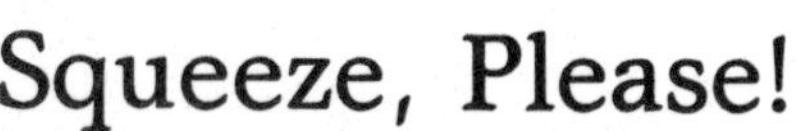

Squeeze, Please!

You need: cornstarch, water, cup or bowl.

- Put 3 tablespoons (45 mL) of cornstarch into a cup or a bowl.
- Dribble in some drops of water.
- When the mixture is pasty, try picking it up. Squeeze it.
- Stop squeezing the mixture and hold it loosely. What happens now?

Instant Fizz

You need: baking soda, vinegar, glass or jar.

- Ask a grownup to help you measure out 3 tablespoons (45 mL) of baking soda into a glass.
- Put the glass in a sink and pour 1/3 cup (75 mL) of vinegar into the glass. Wow!

Bubble Up

You need dishwashing liquid, water, bucket or sink, straw, paper cup, plastic plate.

- Ask a grownup to help you measure out 2/3 cup (150 mL) of dishwashing liquid into a sink or bucket.
- Pour in 4 cups (about 1 L) of water.
- Try out various types of "bubble blowers." Use a straw for a mini-blower. Cut out the bottom of a paper cup for a medium-sized blower, and make a big blower by cutting out the bottom of a plastic plate. How many bubbles can you blow?
- The soap mixture may work even better if it sits for several days.

Balloon Fun

You need: balloons, water.

- On a hot day, ask a grownup to help you fill balloons with water. Make sure you're out-of-doors!
- Toss the water-filled balloons around with friends. Who will be the first to get wet?

Who's Drinking What?

Follow the lines from the toys to see what each one is drinking.

MILK

1 2 3 4

Answer: Bear, 4. Marigold, 1. Humpty, 3. Dumpty, 2.

COOKING

The Missing Cookies

Here is a mystery story that's incomplete. Ask a grownup to read the words. You can help by saying the word for each picture in the story. Can you figure out who took the cookies at the end?

Late one Wednesday night  couldn't get to sleep. He was hungry, too.

"Tomorrow is Imagination Day", he thought as he tossed and turned. "We should do something special for ." And with that he woke up the other toys.

"Let's bake some polka dot  for Polkaroo," said Bear.

"But it's almost midnight," said  .

"How exciting!" said Humpty and Dumpty at the same time. "Look at the  shining through the window," continued Humpty. "I see a  swooping and a , too! If they can be up, why can't we?"

No one could think of a good reason, so all the toys trooped off to the kitchen.

★ ★ ☆ ★ ★

"Polkaroo!" said  cheerfully as he danced through the  the next morning. He stopped in mid-jump.

"Polkaroo," he sighed loudly.

What a mess the kitchen was! The and were still on the counter, flour and sugar were sprinkled on the floor, and the hadn't even been soaked in the .

All the toys were a mess, too, except for . He was fast asleep in bed, with a smile on his face. was the first to wake up. She had fallen asleep, propped against the wall. She rubbed her and looked around. Humpty and Dumpty were sound asleep in the storytelling a on their

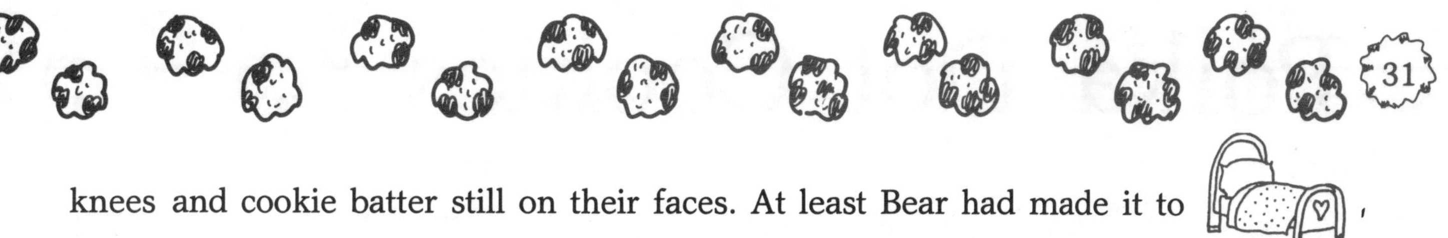

knees and cookie batter still on their faces. At least Bear had made it to ,

thought Marigold.

''Oh, Polkaroo. I know everything is a mess,'' she said, ''but we've made you a

wonderful surprise. Look in the .''

''Polkaroo?'' asked Polkaroo, looking in the jar. It was empty!

''Wake up! Humpty, Dumpty, Bear! We've been robbed! Someone has stolen

Polkaroo's  !'' Marigold shouted.

Look carefully at the big picture to see who took the missing cookies.

Answer: Did you follow the cookie crumb trail to Bear?

Polka Dot Cookies

You need these kitchen items: measuring spoons, a grater, two mixing bowls, a measuring cup, a big stirring spoon, a glass, a cookie sheet, a rack.

You need these ingredients:
1/2 cup shortening (125 mL)
1 cup sugar (250 mL)
1/2 teaspoon salt (2 mL)
1/2 teaspoon grated lemon rind (2 mL)

1 egg
2 tablespoons milk (25 mL)

2 cups flour (500 mL)
1 teaspoon baking powder (5 mL)
1/2 teaspoon baking soda (2 mL)

Ask a grownup to help you preheat the oven to 400°F (200°C).

- Blend together the first four ingredients.
- Now add the egg and milk, and beat.
- Combine the last three ingredients and beat these into the mixture as well.
- Grease a cookie sheet. Drop rounded spoonfuls of the batter onto the pan.
- Grease the bottom of a glass and dip the glass in sugar. Now flatten each cookie with the glass.

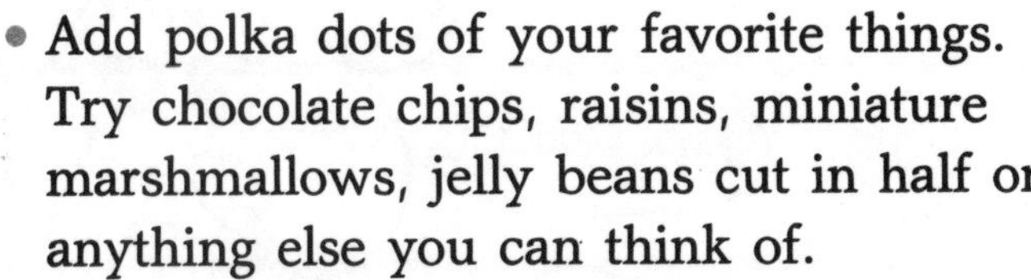

- Add polka dots of your favorite things. Try chocolate chips, raisins, miniature marshmallows, jelly beans cut in half or anything else you can think of.

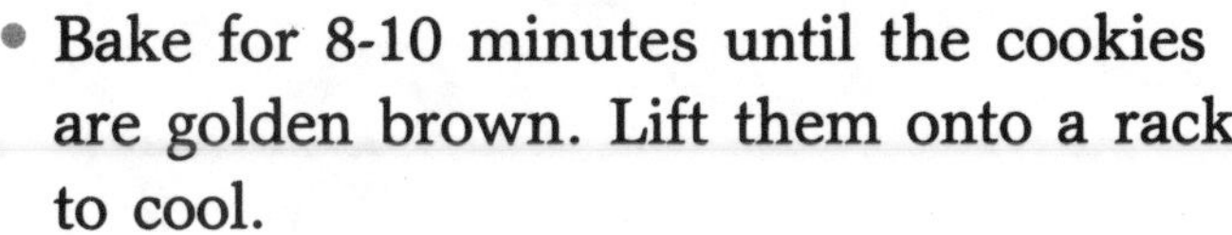

- Bake for 8-10 minutes until the cookies are golden brown. Lift them onto a rack to cool.

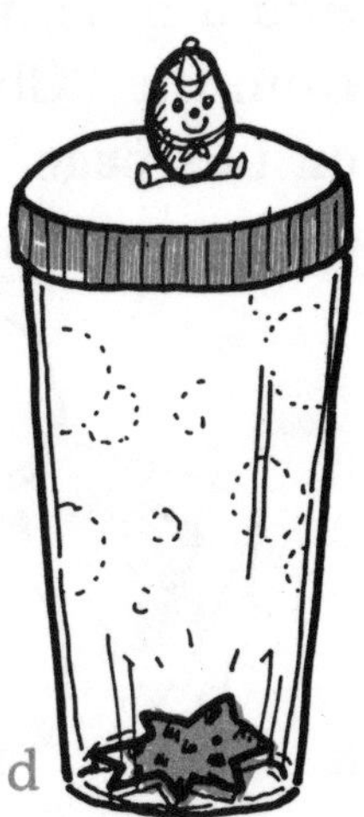

Cookie Count

Circle the correct answer for each question.

1. Which cookie jar has the most cookies?
   a b c d
2. Which cookie jar has the least cookies?
   a b c d
3. How many cookies are there in all?
   5 9 13 15

Answer: 1. c. 2. d. 3. 13 (a baker's dozen).

Super Snacks

Caterpillar Creations

You need: celery, cream cheese or other spread, knife, food items for decorating.

- Ask a grownup to cut short pieces of celery to make caterpillar bodies.

- Fill the celery with cream cheese or cheese spread.

- Add eyes, antennae and legs. Use any or all of the things mentioned in "Choose Your Own."

Happy Faces

You need: bread, peanut butter or other spread, knife, food items for decorating.

- Spread peanut butter or cream cheese on bread.

- Add a nose, mouth and eyes. Take ideas from the "Choose Your Own" section on this page.

Choose Your Own

All of these things make tasty decorations for your caterpillars and happy faces:

Can you think of other things to use?

Cool Cubes

You need: ice cube tray, fruit juice, fresh fruit, string.

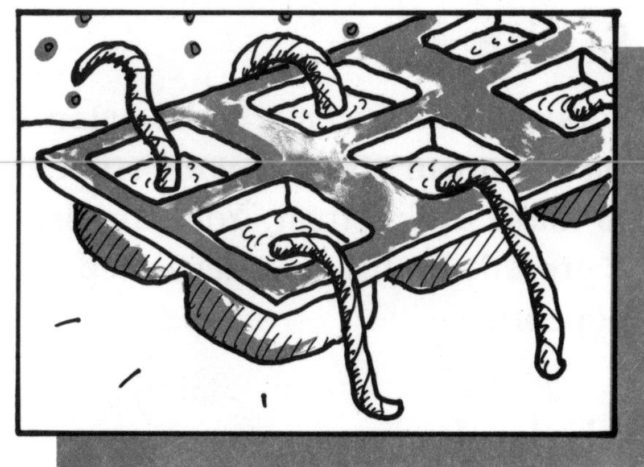

- Ask a grownup to help you fill an ice cube tray with your favorite fruit juice.
- Add a piece of fresh fruit to each. (Strawberries, raspberries or blueberries work well.)
- Place a piece of string in each cube.
- Put the tray in the freezer and wait 4-5 hours.
- Ask for help in removing the cubes from the tray. Dangle one in front of your mouth and slurp it up. Mmm, mmm good!

Frozen Banana

You need: a banana, foil.

- Peel a banana, wrap it in foil and put it in the freezer.
- Take it out later for a super-cool snack.

Popping Popcorn

Pop It

You need: popcorn kernels, oil, heavy pan.

- Be sure to ask a grownup to help you heat butter or grease in a heavy pan.
- Cover the bottom of the pan with one layer of kernels.
- Put the lid on the pan and start shaking it over high heat. (Be patient — it may take a while for the popping to begin.)
- When the popping sound stops, pour the popcorn into a bowl.
- Add a little salt and some melted butter if you like.

String It

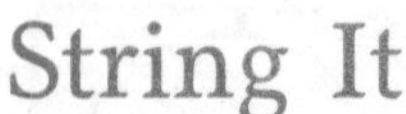

Popcorn doesn't have to be eaten to be fun. You can string it with cranberries to make a bird treat. You can also make a present by filling a decorated jar with popcorn.

Hide It

At least two people are needed for this game but as many as you want can play. Ask a family member or friend to leave the room while you hide one piece of popcorn. Part of it has to be easily seen. Ask the person to come back and look for the popcorn. If you like, help the person by saying "Pop." The closer he or she gets to the popcorn, say "Pop" more often and faster. Once the popcorn is spotted, it is your turn to leave the room.

Popcorn Hunt

There is lots of popcorn in the two bowls and the gift jar. Can you spot at least 17 other pieces of popcorn hidden here?

Pet Puzzle

Help each of the pets find the most appropriate food for it. Which pets might eat the leftover foods?

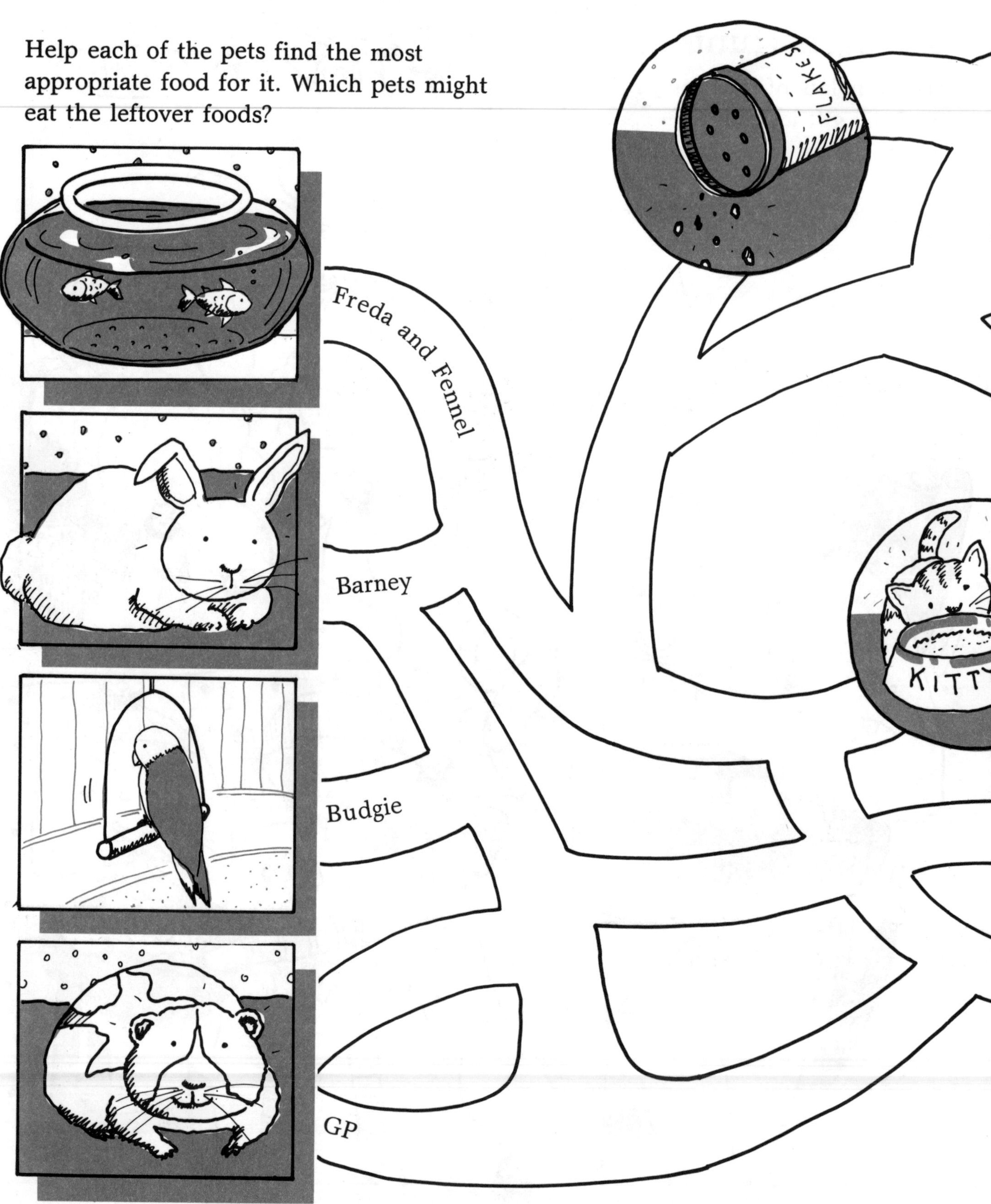

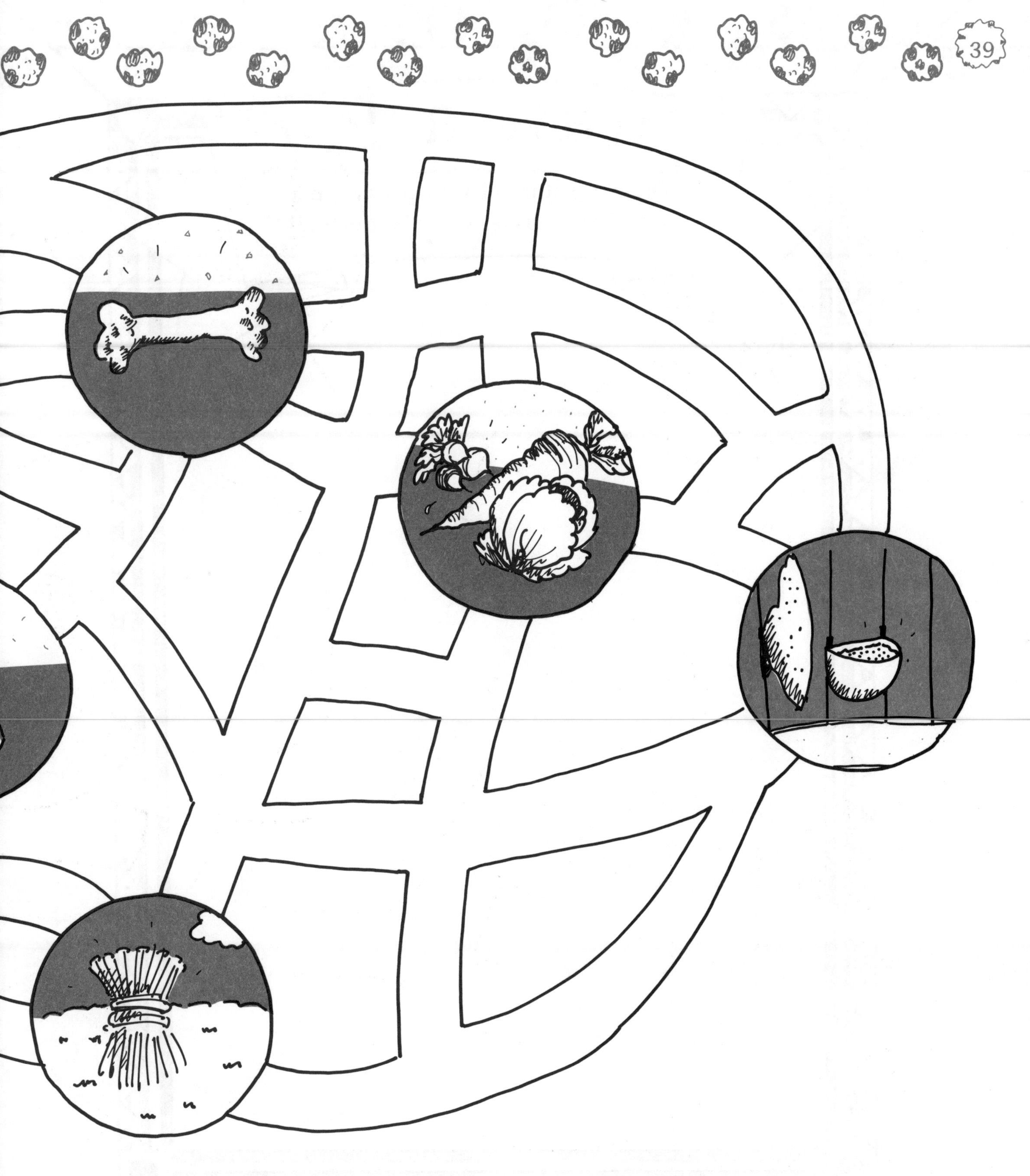

Answer: Did you take Freda and Fennel to the fishflakes, Barney to the hay, Budgie to the birdseed and GP to the vegetables? Cats like catfood and dogs like bones.

Draw a Pet

Draw a picture of your pet or a pet you'd like to have. What is it eating?

BUILDING

Winter Fun

Make a ball of snow in your hands and see if it holds its shape. If it does, the snow is perfect for building snowmen, snow forts or snow creatures.

Snowman Snacks

Make a snowman for the birds. Use food to make the face, buttons and other decorations. Birds like to eat raisins, prunes, orange and lemon peel, nuts, celery, carrots, crackers, and of course, birdseed!

Tree Treats

Decorate a tree in your backyard or park with bird treats.

- Pine-cones rolled in peanut butter and birdseed are great.
- Ask a grownup to help you string cranberries and popcorn together.
- Put some fat or lard in an onion bag to hang on the tree.
- Make a bird-feeder out of a milk carton. Ask a grownup to cut a hole in the lower third of the box. Fill the bottom of the box with birdseed or sunflower seeds.

Snow Slide

Build a huge snowhill and slide down it once or twice.

- When your slide is smooth, ask a grownup to sprinkle water on it with a hose. Let the water freeze, and sprinkle on another layer of water.
- When the slide is good and icy, away you go! Depending on the weather, you may have to wait overnight to try out your slide.

Summer Fun

Super Sandysaurus

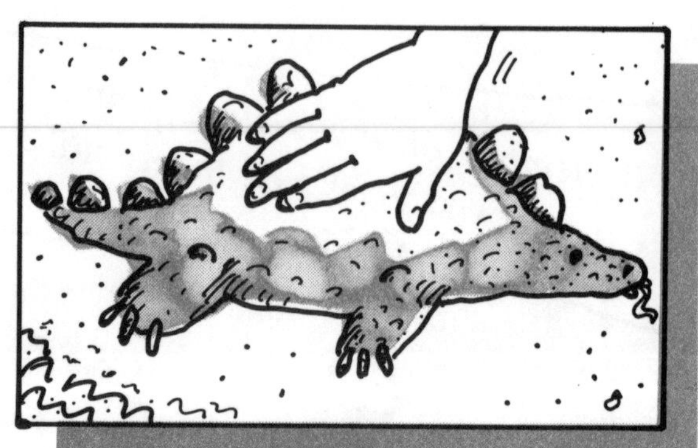

Make some of your own crazy sand creatures.

- Make a firm mound of wet sand for a body, tail, legs and feet.
- Give the creature eyes, fur or feathers, ears and a mouth. Use driftwood, shells, stones, beach plants or flowers, and anything else you'd like to use for decoration.

Pebble Picture

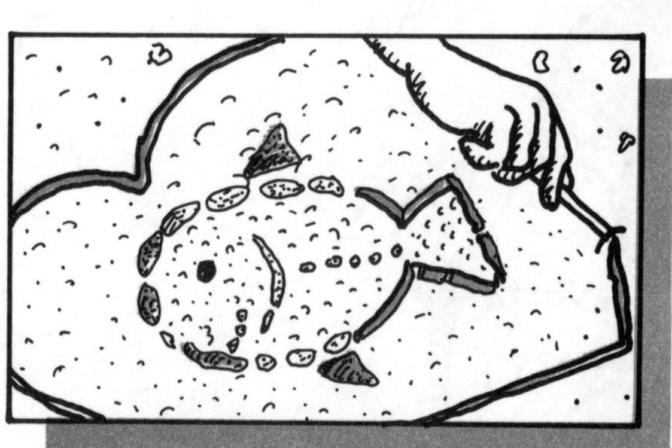

- Find a flat section of wet sand. Ask a grownup to help you draw a picture-frame outline in the sand with a stick.
- Make a picture out of small stones within the picture frame. Try using small twigs or shells for your next beach picture.

I Spy

Look carefully to find the five things hidden in the picture below.

Build a Boat

Create a boat out of almost anything — plastic or styrofoam food containers, tart tins, popsicle sticks glued together, milk cartons.... Use plasticine to anchor a popsicle stick or twig mast to the boat and tape on a paper sail. Then, heave ho!

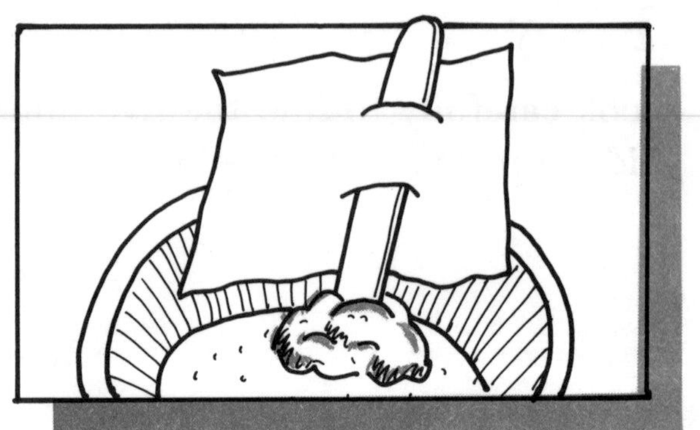

Which Are the Same?

Look carefully to find two boats that are exactly alike.

A Sailor Went to Sea

A sailor went to sea
To see what he could see
And all that he could see
Was the deep blue sea.

You need these kitchen items: a pot, a plate, a cloth, a spoon.

You need these ingredients:

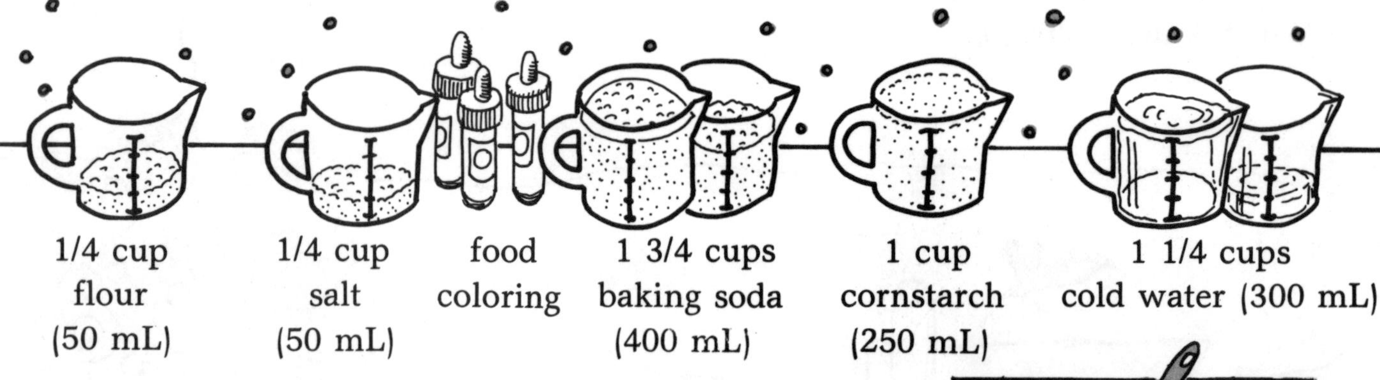

- Ask a grownup to help you heat all the ingredients (except the food coloring) in a pot over medium heat.

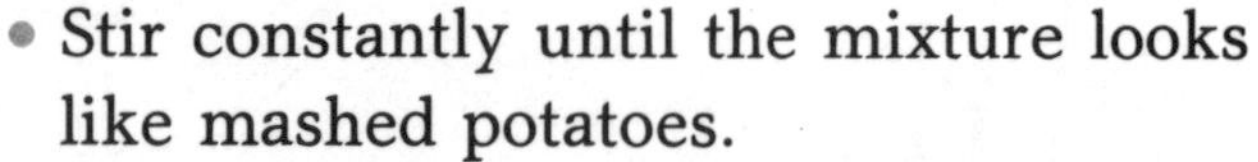

- Stir constantly until the mixture looks like mashed potatoes.

- Put the clay on a plate, cover it with a cloth and let it cool.

- To color the clay, separate it into three or four smaller mounds. Add a few drops of food coloring and work them into the mounds. For a stronger color, add more drops.

Who Doesn't Belong?

All of these creatures except one build nests or homes for their babies. Which one doesn't?

Answer: A zebra. Soon after it is born, a baby zebra is up and walking with the herd. Its home is a wide, grassy plain.

Boxes Can't Be Beat!

Boxes come in all shapes and sizes, and they can become almost anything you want. Here are a few ideas. Can you think of any others?

- Make dollhouse furniture out of old match boxes. You can also use a match box to store goodies in when you're traveling.

- An empty tissue box can become a ''store-all stuffer'' for your crayons or small toys. Or you can decorate it with homemade wrapping paper to make a special gift box for Christmas or birthdays.

- Draw a picture and paste it on an old cereal box. Ask a grownup to help you cut the picture into wacky shapes of different sizes. Can you put your puzzle together again? Use another cereal box for storing your homemade puzzles.

- You can use cartons to make a train for your stuffed animals. Huge appliance boxes can become clubhouses or forts. Ask a grownup to help you cut a door and windows in the bigger boxes.

How Many?

There are at least 16 full rectangles and 5 full squares hidden here. Do you see any others?

This is the House that Jack Built

Ask a grownup to read the words in this nursery rhyme. Can you fill in the blanks?

This is the house that Jack built.

This is the malt
That lay in the _______
That Jack built.

This is the rat
That ate the malt
That lay in the _______ that Jack built.

This is the cat
That killed the rat
That ate the _______
That lay in the house that Jack built.

This is the dog
That worried the _______
That killed the _______
That ate the malt
That lay in the _______ that Jack built.

This is the cow with the crumpled horn
That tossed the _______
That worried the cat
That killed the _______
That ate the malt
That lay in the _______ that Jack built.

This is the _______ all forlorn
That milked the _______ with the crumpled horn
That tossed the _______
That worried the _______
That killed the _______
That ate the _______
That lay in the _______ that Jack built.

rat

cat

house

dog

cow

house

house

malt

cow

rat

maiden

house

rat

Jack

rat

dog

malt

cat

DRESSING UP

54 Find the Hats and Shoes

Today Polkaroo and his three friends want to dress up. Draw lines from each of them to the hats and shoes that complete their costumes. If you wish, color in the costumes.

Answer: Firefighter, 1,d. Doctor, 7,c. Hockey Player, 5,b. Clown, 6,g.

Make a Puppet

Sock Puppets

Make some hand puppets out of old socks. Ask a grownup to help you sew or glue on a fabric mouth, some button eyes and woolen hair. Then sing a song like "Old Macdonald Had a Farm" or act out a rhyme like "Jack and Jill."

Mitten Puppets

Use odd or old mittens to make hand puppets. Decorate the puppets with some of the things mentioned in "Choose Your Own." Then put on a play.

Choose Your Own

Use some of these items to decorate your puppets.

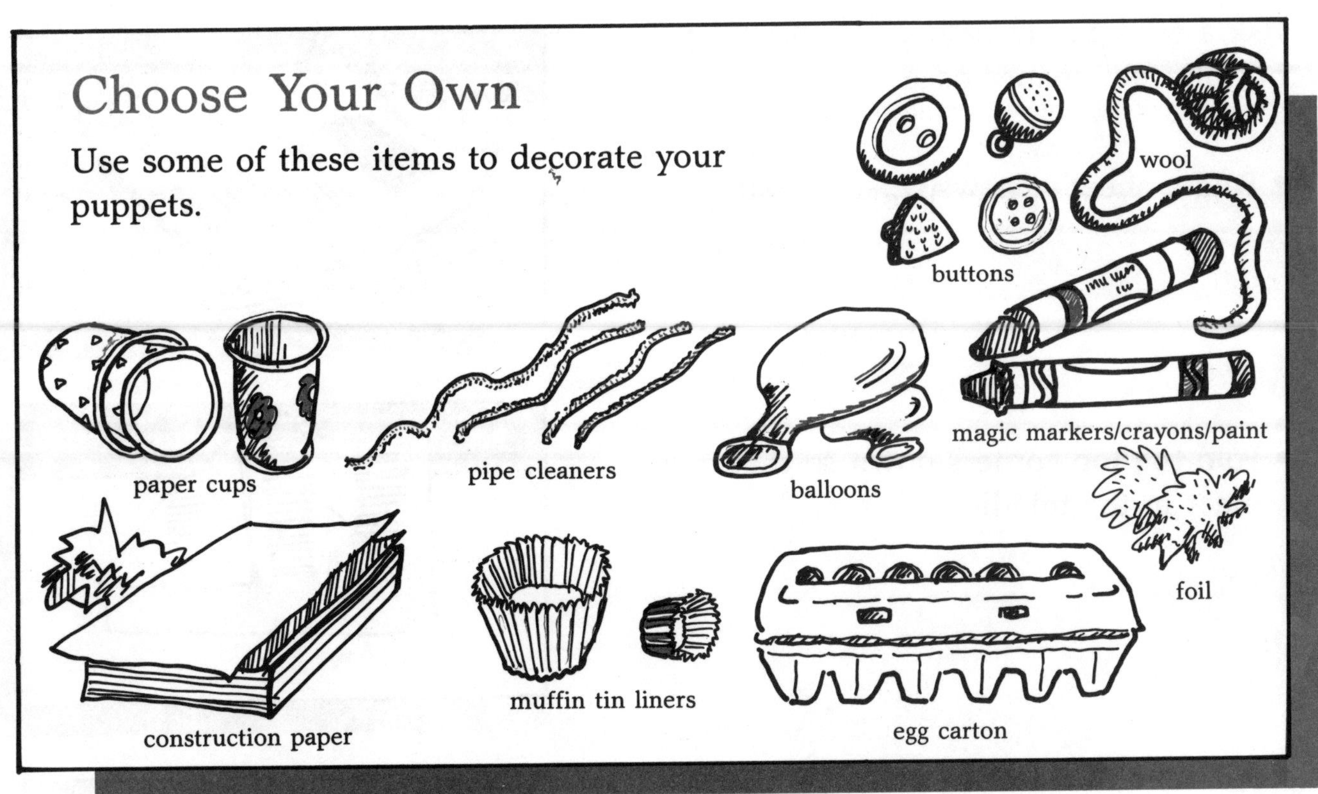

Riddle Match-up

These hand puppets are asking some riddles but they've forgotten which answers go with which questions. Draw lines to help them find the answers.

3. What's tall, green, has polka dots and comes in a jar?

4. What did Marigold's right sock say to her left foot?

c. When it's raining cats and dogs!

d. Milk and chirpios!

Answer: 1, c. 2, d. 3, a. 4, b.

Make a Hat

Ask a grownup to help you make a hat out of a newspaper page.

- Fold a sheet of newspaper in half.

- Fold the top corners down so that they meet in the middle.

- Fold one of the bottom flaps in half and upward.
- Fold the bottom flap up again.
- Turn the sheet of newspaper over and do the same on the other side. Try on your new hat.

Make a Mask

Make a Paper Plate Mask

You need: a paper plate, scissors, tape, a wooden spoon (or clothespin), decorating items.

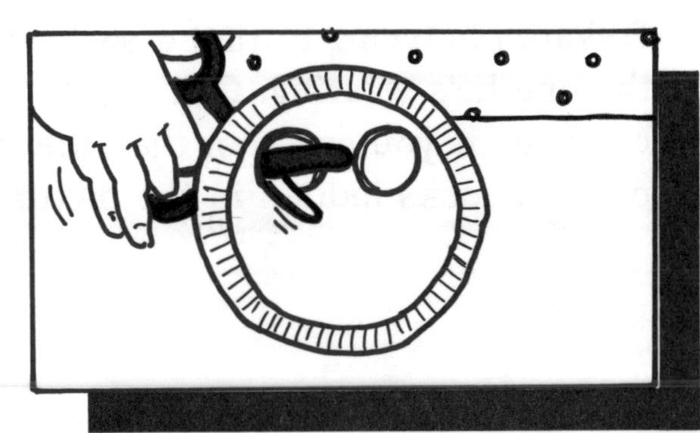

- Ask a grownup to cut eye holes in a paper plate.

- Use heavy tape to fasten a wooden spoon to the back of the plate. A clothespin also works well as a handle. Decorate your mask.

Make a Paper Bag Mask

You need: a paper bag that fits over your head, newspaper, scissors, tape or glue, decorating items.

- Stuff newspaper in the bag so that it will stay upright on your head.
- Ask a grownup to make large holes for the eyes.
- Decorate your mask.

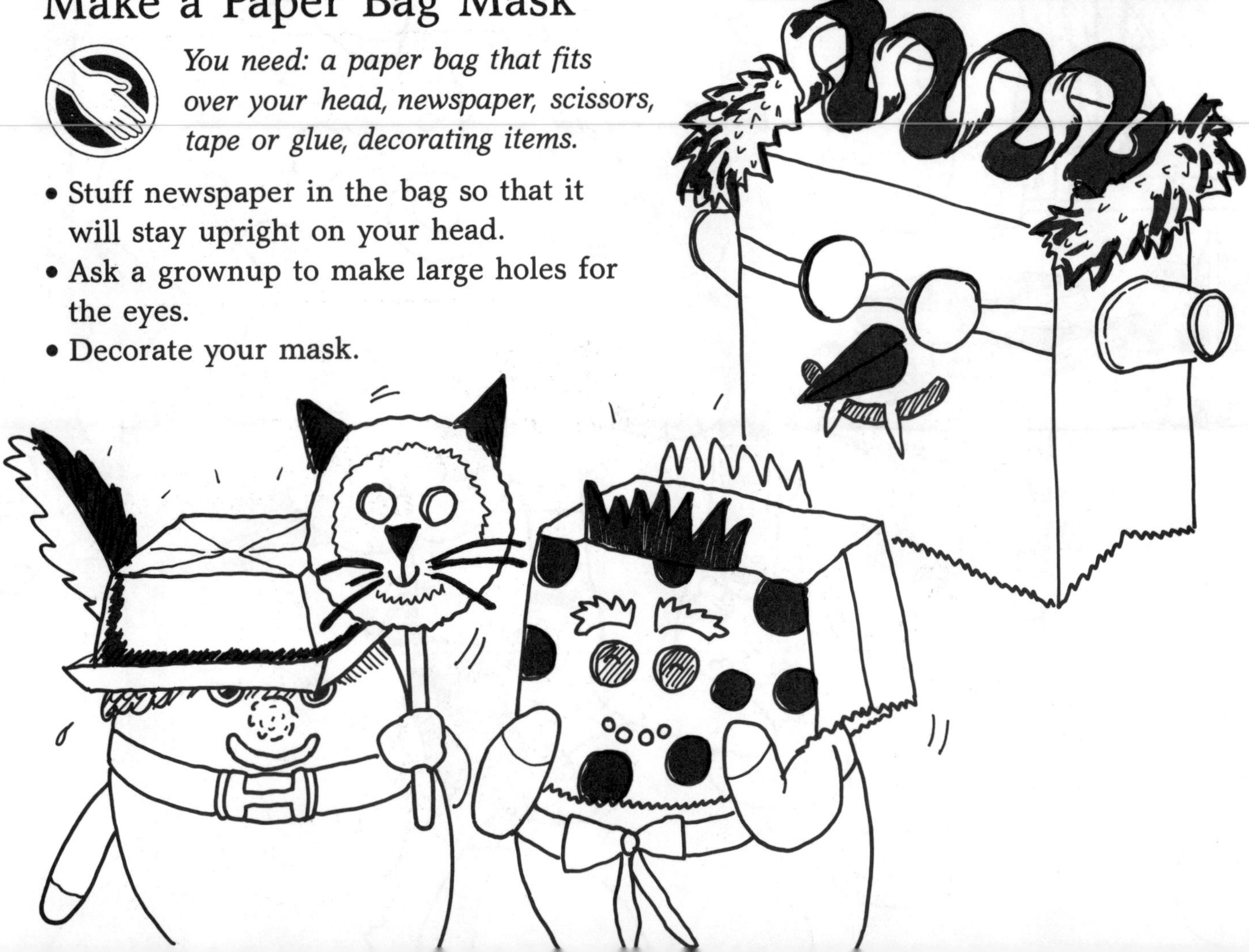

60 Sock Search

Polkaroo is trying to find a sock to match the one he's wearing. Can you help him? Now see if you can spot the other four pairs of socks hidden in the picture.

MOVING

The Storytime Mouse

Ask a grownup to read the story. While you're listening, look at the pictures along the paths. There are several ways to follow, but only one path matches the words in the story. Can you find it? Listen carefully!

Once upon a time a tiny mouse lived in a small country library. She loved books, and after the library was closed each night, out she scurried to read. One night she turned the very last page of the very last book. What would she read now? "Perhaps I can find a much larger library if I travel to the city," thought the mouse. So she packed her bag with a piece of cheese, her reading glasses and her great-grandfather's watch, and she set forth.

The mouse hadn't gone far when she realized she was going to need help in getting to the city. Just then a big farm truck rumbled to a stop beside her. "Better than nothing," thought the mouse, and she climbed into the back of the truck.

The truck was crammed with mounds of crisp farm produce on its way to market. There were lettuces and baby carrots, fresh green beans and garden peas, giant prickly gooseberries and ripe, red raspberries. "What luck!" thought the mouse. She settled down to a feast as the old truck rumbled along.

The mouse was dozing off when the truck jerked to a stop and then backed up. The tailgate slammed down, and a board was laid across it into a train car. Brrrr! It was a refrigerated train car and no place for a mouse to hide. It was time to find another way to travel.

The mouse scampered down the edge of the train track to another open train car. This was the baggage compartment. "Perfect!" thought the mouse as she ran inside. From a dark, quiet corner she watched the baggage lady slide the big door shut. "So far, so good," she thought. "Going to the city is as easy as cheese pie!"

The train raced through the countryside. For a while, the mouse amused herself by reading all the baggage tags on the suitcases. Suddenly she heard a sound behind her. The mouse whipped around. Eeek! It was a cat!

The cat pounced, and the mouse jumped backwards. Then they both raced off at breakneck speeds. "Where, oh where can I hide?" worried the mouse. Round a stack of boxes she went, and over a suitcase. Oh, no! The cat was gaining on her. Ahead lay a wire cage. The mouse took a deep breath and dove through the bars and into a warm furry ball.

The cat snarled outside the cage and began to pace back and forth. Meanwhile the mouse quickly backed

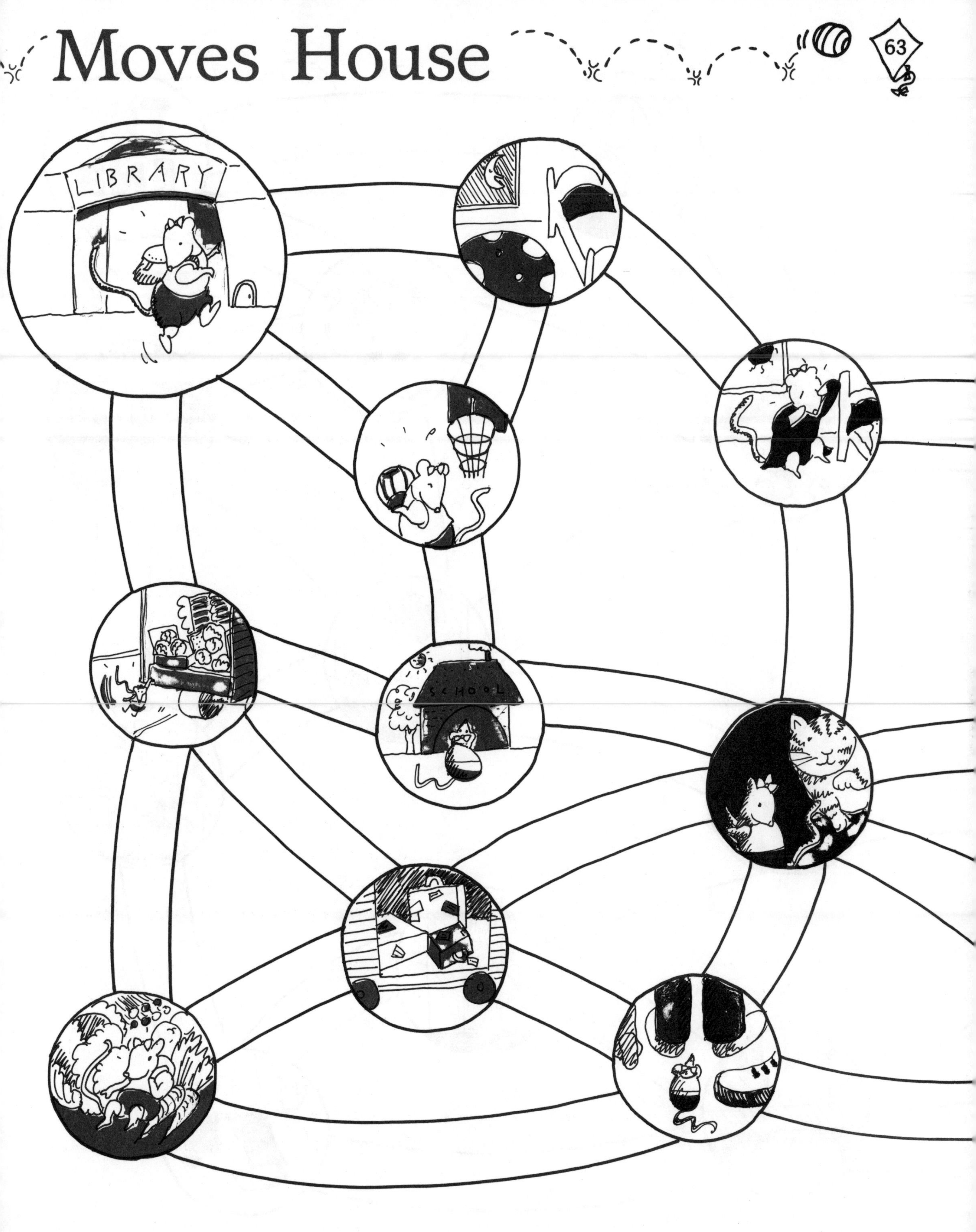
LIBRARY
SCHOOL

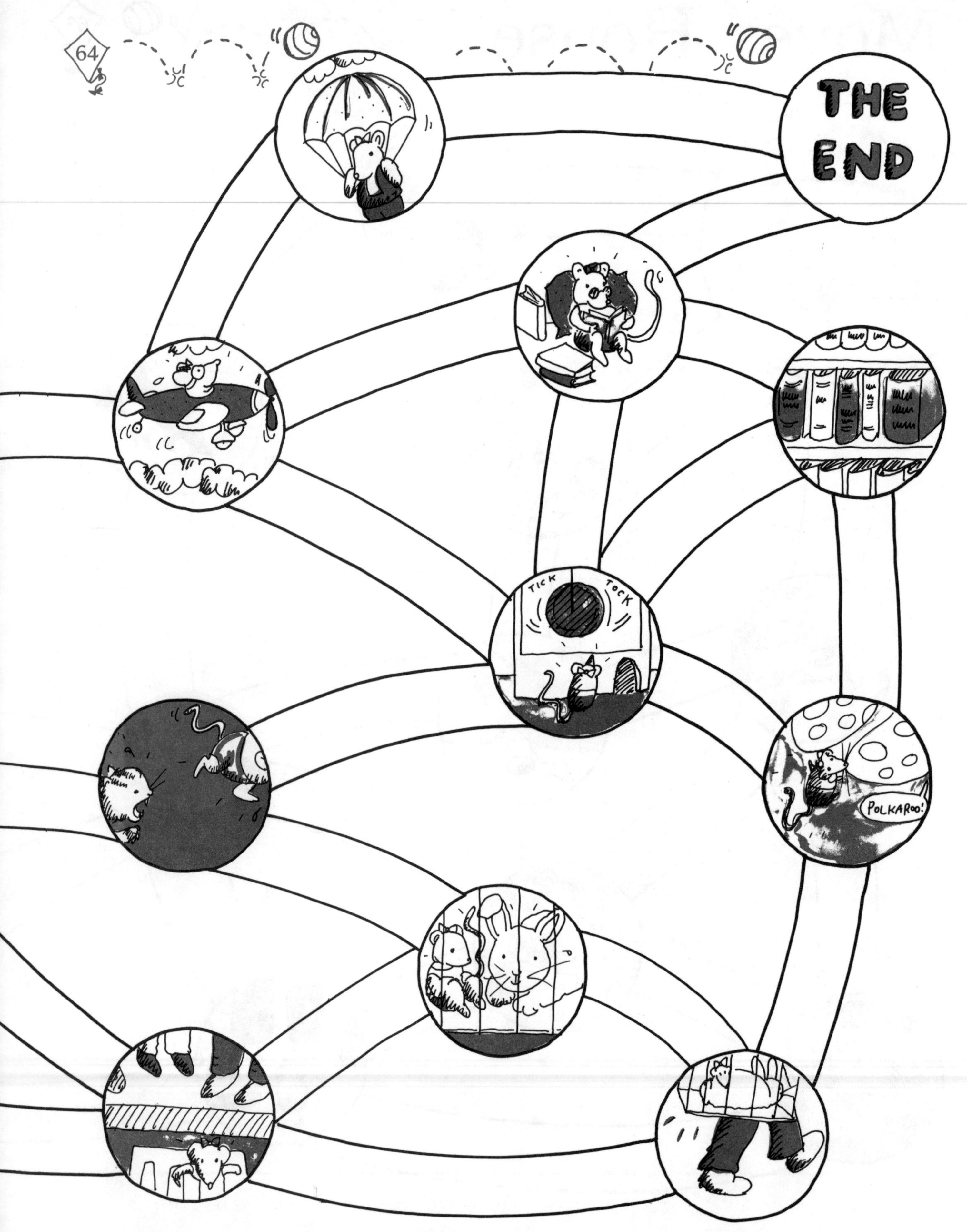
THE END
TICK
TOCK
POLKAROO!

away from the furry ball. "Thank goodness," she sighed. "It's only a bunny." She apologized to the rabbit for her sudden arrival and and asked if she could stay until the cat left. When the rabbit said, "Of course!" the mouse drifted off to sleep.

Suddenly she woke up. She was in mid-air — what was happening? Uh, oh. The train had stopped, and now the cage was being carried off the baggage car. Honking and hubbub surrounded her. The mouse had made it to the city! The rabbit now told her that she lived in a very nice place indeed, and she was sure the mouse would be welcome. "But does she live in a library?" wondered the mouse.

No. Instead Barney the bunny lived in a warm, cozy shed in a backyard. She shared the shed with a guinea pig named GP, Budgie (a budgie, of course) and Freda and Fennel, two elegant goldfish. They were the friendliest creatures the mouse had ever met, but there was not a book in sight. After a few days, the mouse explained that she just *had* to find some books to read, for that was why she had journeyed so far. "Try going through the Polka Dot Door," chirped Budgie. "It's a very special place and there are bound to be books somewhere inside."

"It's worth a try," thought the mouse, and the next morning she slipped under the door. Inside she saw a cheerful room with a rocker in front of a bay window, a big toy chest, a grandfather clock ... and a monster! "Yikes!" shrieked the mouse as a huge, green, polka-dotted creature grinned down at her. The mouse ran for the only hole in sight.

A gentle tick-tock, tick-tock was all the mouse could now hear. She had run into the bottom of the grandfather clock. And what a clock it was! It was filled with storybooks, row upon row piled as far as the mouse could see. Budgie was right — this *was* a special place! But what about that monster?

The mouse peeked shyly through the hole to see the monster dancing with four laughing toys. "Polkaroo!" chuckled the monster.

"It must be a friendly monster," thought the mouse. "I guess I'll stay. Maybe I could even share some of these wonderful stories with those toys and even with the monster."

And that's how the mouse came through the Polka Dot Door to live in the grandfather clock. In time she became known as the Storytime Mouse because every day she rang a magic bell inviting everyone to come and hear her stories. Needless to say, she lived happily ever after.

See Time Move

Ask a grownup to help you make your own sun clock or sundial.

You need: a flowerpot, earth or playdough, a marker, construction paper, tape, a pencil, a timing device.

- Fill a pot with earth or playdough and stick a pencil in the center.
- Wrap a piece of construction paper around the base of the pot.
- Set the pot in a place that is sunny all day long.
- Starting on the hour, mark where the pencil shadow falls on the edge of the pot. Continue the line down the base of the pot to the bottom.
- Ask a grownup to help you set an alarm clock or the timer on a stove so that it rings in an hour.
- When the timer rings, mark the new place where the shadow now falls. Repeat this process all day until you have the hours marked off on the pot.
- WARNING: If you move your sun clock, you'll have to start marking the pot all over again.

What Time Is It?

Fill in the clock faces with the times of the day that you normally do these things.

Waking up

Playing

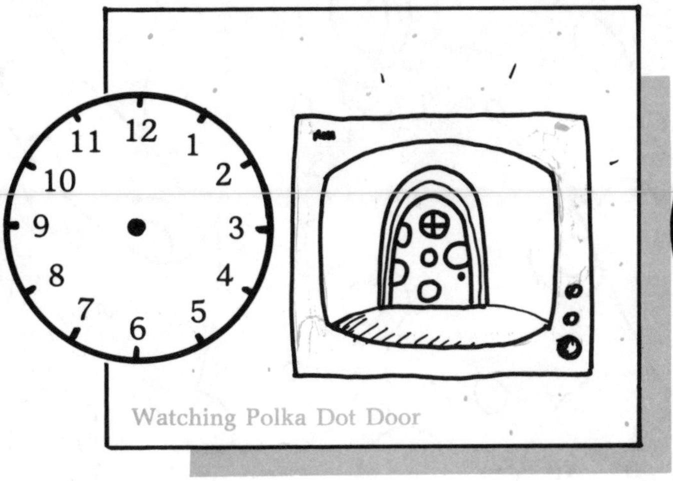

Watching Polka Dot Door

Eating lunch

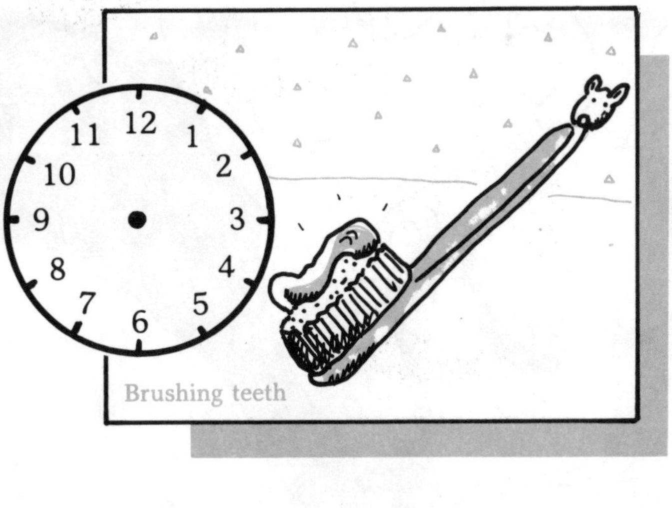

Brushing teeth

Going to bed

On The Move!

There are many different ways of moving. Name the ones you see here. Which is the one movement that people can only do in a machine?

How many times can you hop on your left foot?

Answer: People cannot fly by themselves.

Moving

Try to do all the actions mentioned here.

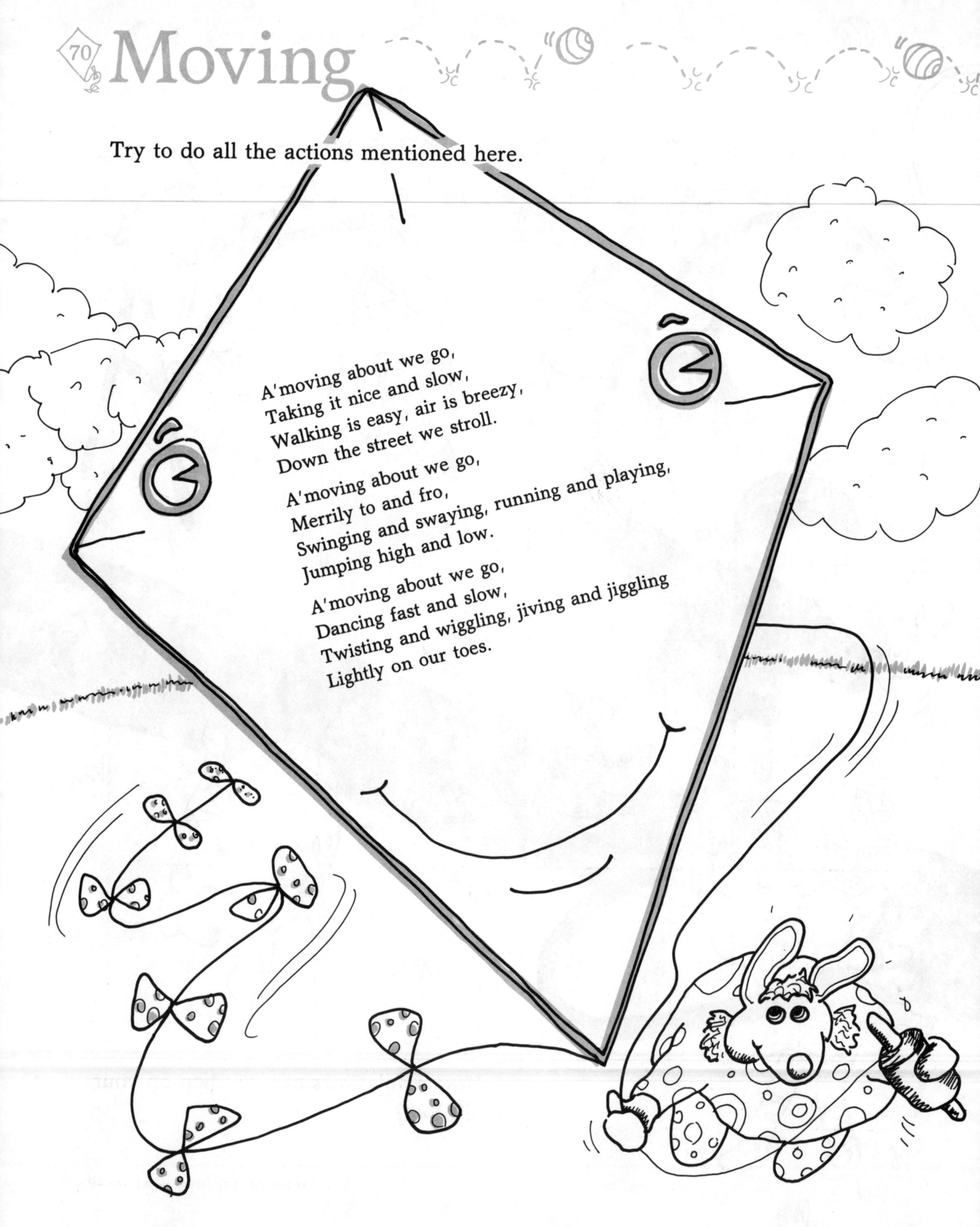

Which One Is Different?

Look carefully at the animals in each row. Think about how they move. Which one moves differently from the others in the row?

Answer: The wasp doesn't hop, the seagull doesn't swim, the bat doesn't run. Did you notice that these three all fly?

Make a Mobile

You need: plastic straws, string or yarn, small metal objects.

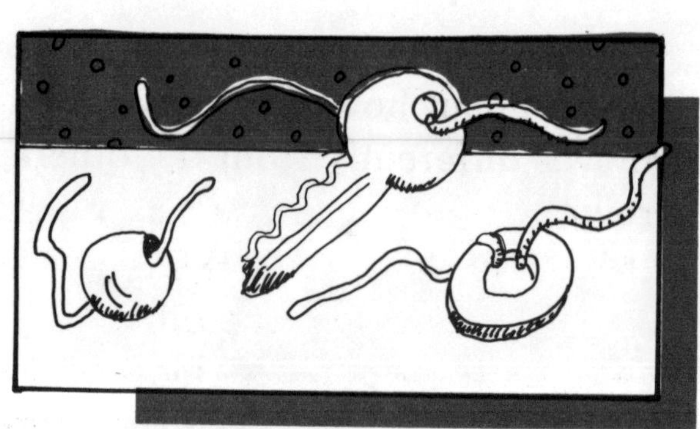

- Ask a grownup to help you hang plastic straws from each other, so that you have a triangular-shaped mobile. Hang some strings from the frame.
- Tie old keys, paper clips, tart tins and any other small metal objects to the ends of the loose strings.
- Move the strings along the straws until the mobile is balanced.
- Hang it in a window and wait for a breeze to blow.

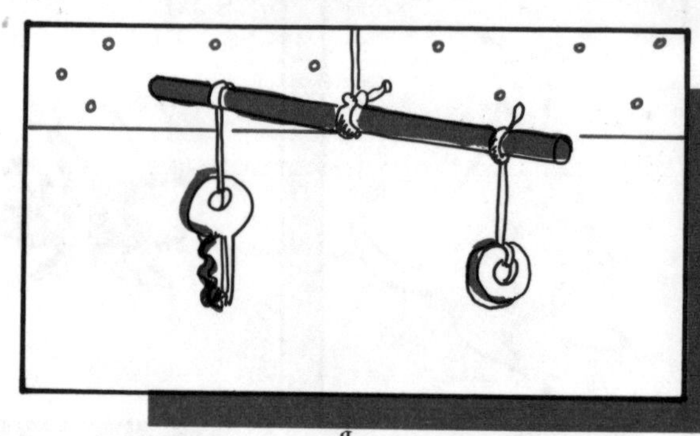

Find Two the Same

Which two objects in the mobile are exactly the same?

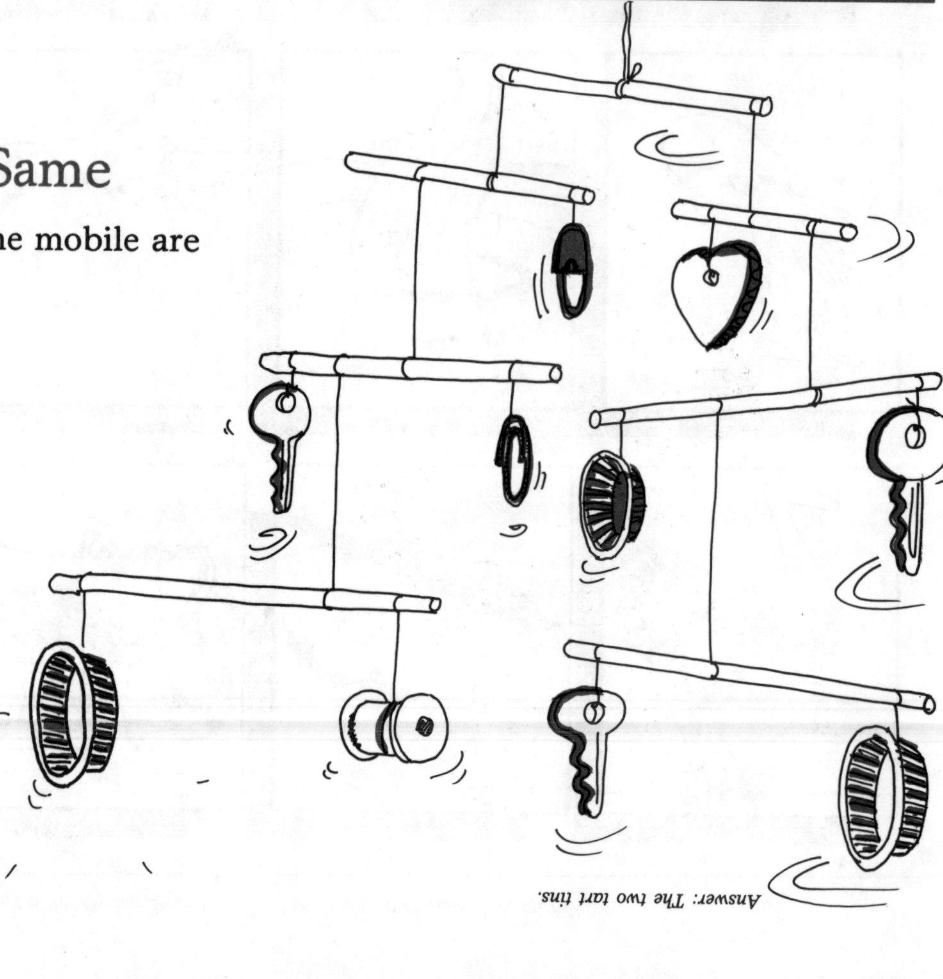

Answer: The two tart tins.

Blow Football

You need: a ping-pong ball (or styrofoam chip), two straws, a friend.

- Clear a table and place a ping-pong ball in the middle.
- Stand on one side of the table and ask a friend to stand on the other.
- At the count of three, blow at the ball through the straws. Whoever can blow the ball off the table is the winner of that round.
- Play the best three out of five games to determine the grand champ.

Count the Wheels

Wheels help lots of things move quickly and easily. How many wheels can you count here?

PAINTING

Color and See

The toys have just mixed up some paint in an egg carton. Ask a grownup to tell you which colors belong in each egg carton cup, and color the cups in. Then match the patterns in the egg carton cups with the identical patterns in the toys' mural, and color in their picture.

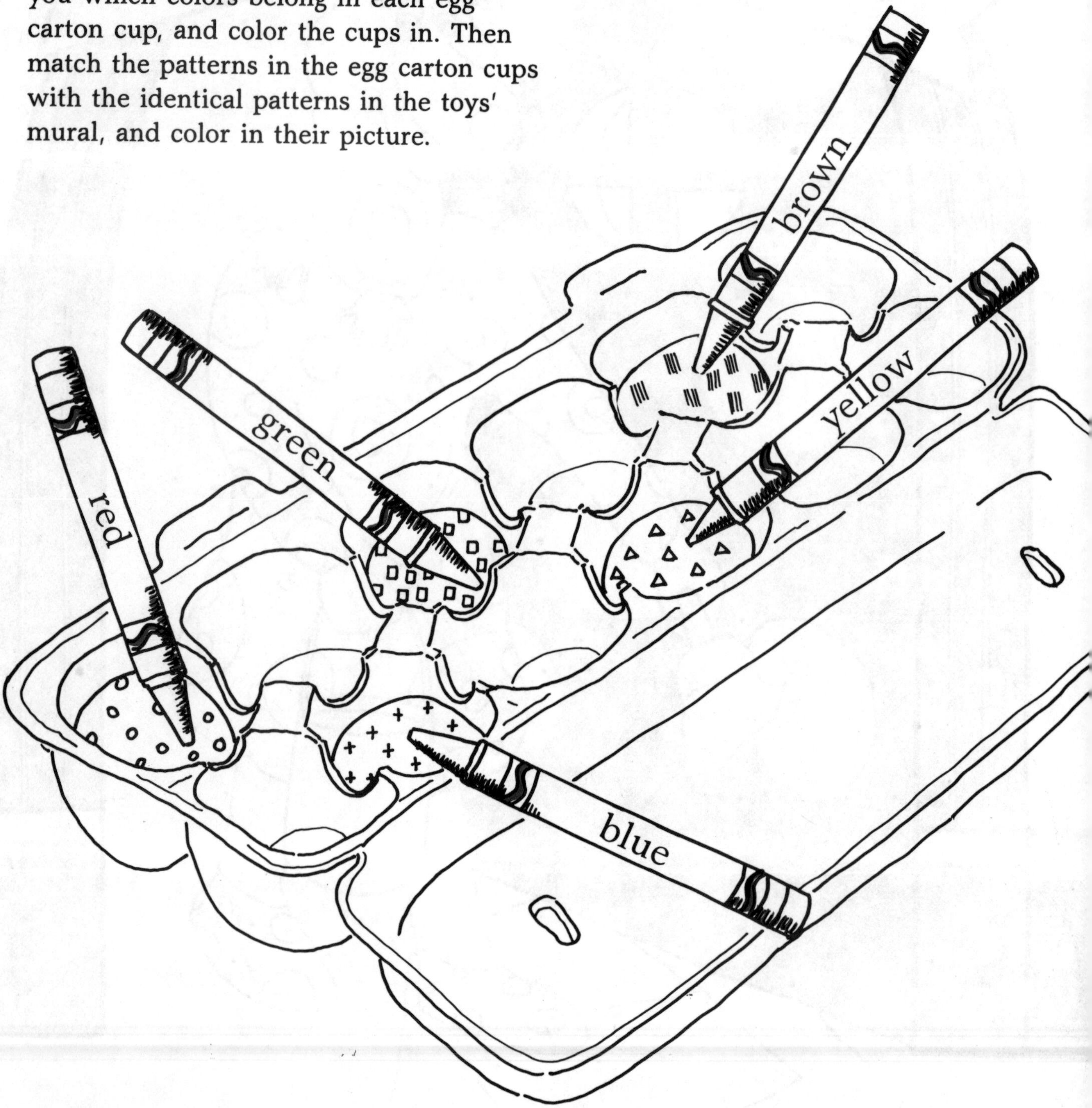

brown
yellow
green
red
blue

Color Combinations

Ask a grownup to tell you which colors go in the labeled boxes in each line. To fill in the blank box, color it with the first color in the line. Then color it over with the second color. What new color have you made?

red + yellow =

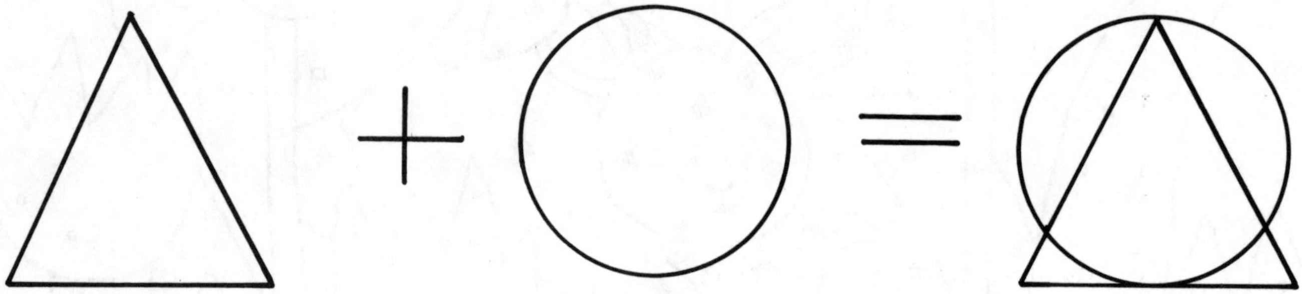

blue + red =

blue + yellow =

Answer: 1, orange. 2, purple. 3, green.

Things to Use

Drawings can be made from just about anything. Circle the things that you have used to make a picture.

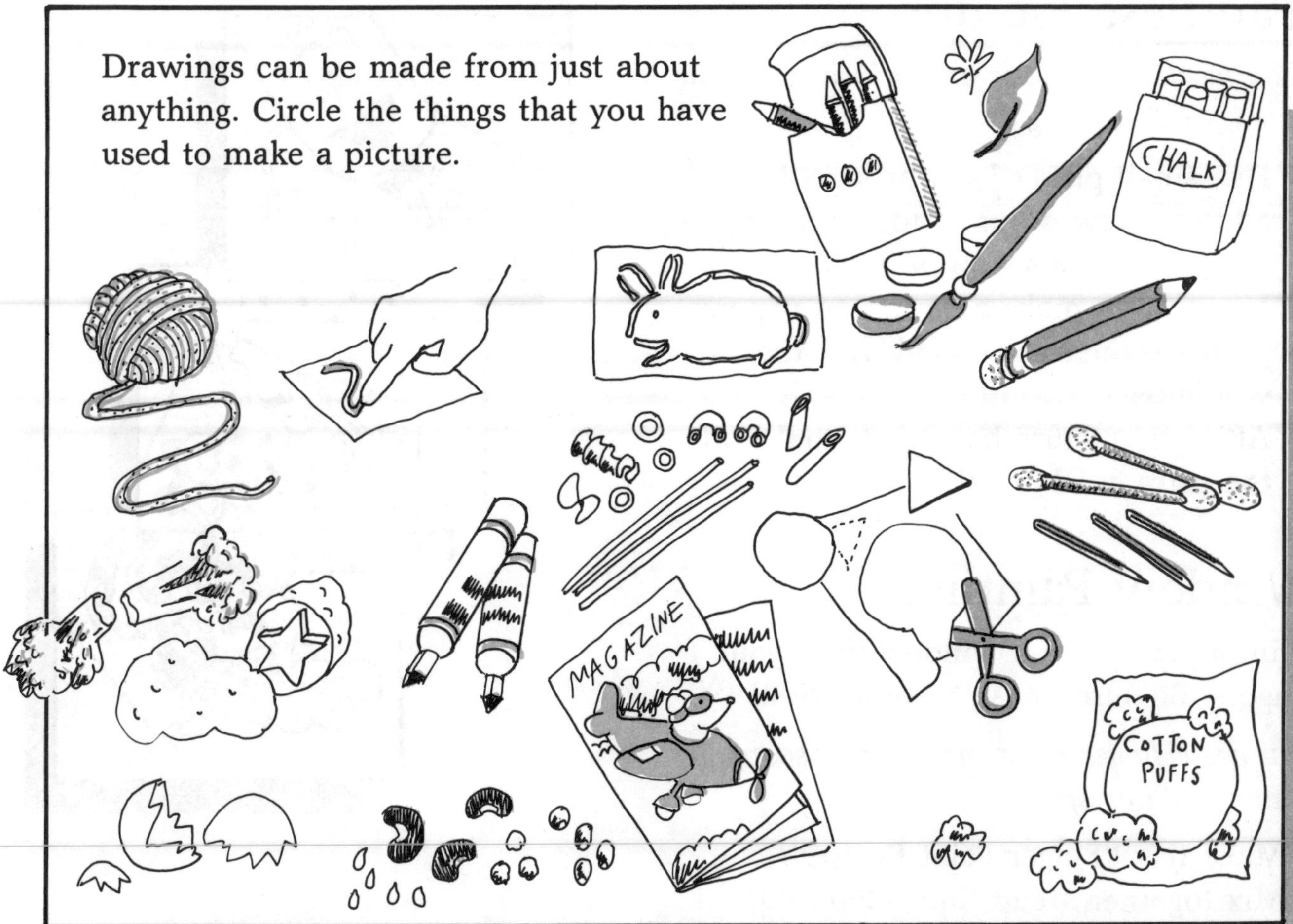

Fresh Prints

You need: fruit or vegetable pieces, paper, poster paint.

- Ask a grownup to cut some vegetables or fruit into pieces.
- Use these pieces to make some print pictures. Dip the cut side into a dish of poster paint, then press it onto a sheet of paper.
- Try using apples, potatoes, carrots, radishes, cauliflower, broccoli.... What else can you think of?

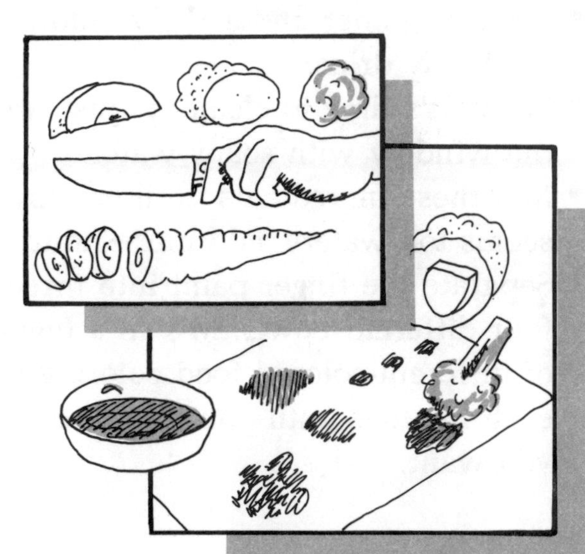

Painting Pointers

Paintless Picture

You need: glue, paper or cardboard, salt or sand, food coloring.

- Dye small piles of salt or sand by adding a few drops of food coloring and stirring with a spoon or stick.
- Use glue to make a design on paper.
- Sprinkle the salt or sand over the whole page.
- After the picture has dried, shake off the extra sand or salt.

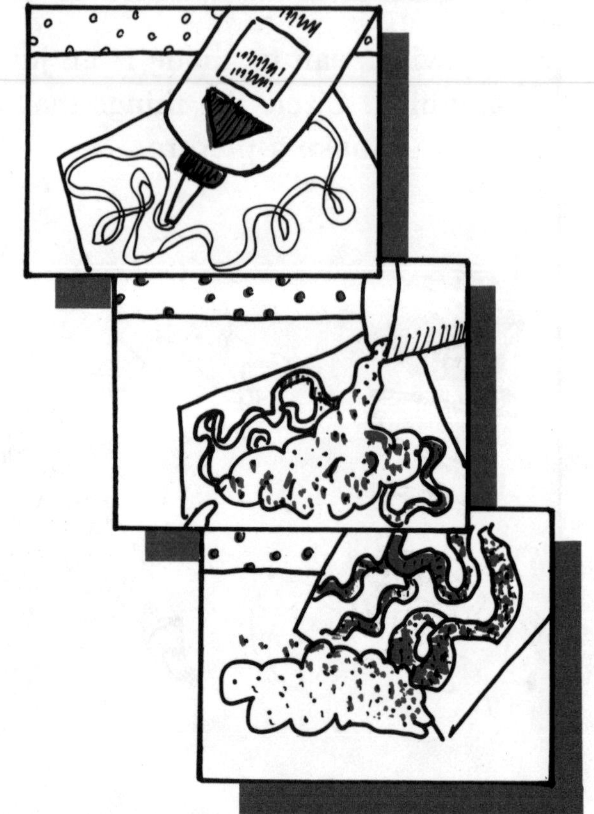

Window Painting

Paint a picture on a window with your fingers. Be sure to ask an adult first!

You need: finger paint, newspaper, soapy water, cloth or sponge.

- Make this "Finger Paint Recipe":
  Mix together 1 cup flour (250 mL),
  3/4 cup water (175 mL) and
  2 tablespoons cooking oil (25 mL).
- Put newspaper under the window to catch any drips.
- When it's time to clean up, just wash the window with soapy water.
- Mix these ingredients until creamy. If it seems too watery, add more flour.
- Separate the finger paint into three or four different bowls. Mix in a few drops of different-colored food coloring into each mixture until you have the color you want.

Something's the Same

The toys are all making pictures in different ways, but their pictures show one thing that is the same. Can you spot what it is?

Answer: They've all drawn a sun!

Eggs-tra Fun

You need: eggs, food coloring, water, markers, decorating items, glue.

- Ask a grownup to help you hard-boil or blow some eggs.
- Mix a few drops of food coloring into some water.
- Dip the eggs one by one.
- When the shells have dried, use markers to decorate them.
- You can also glue on pieces of felt and other cloth scraps to make extra-fancy eggs.

How to Blow an Egg

You need: a pin or large needle, a bowl.

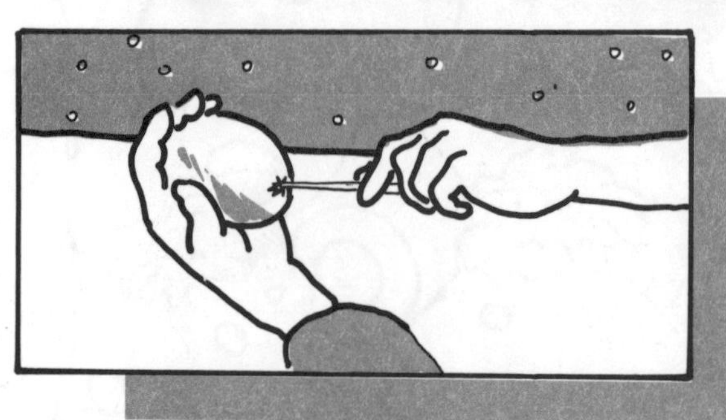

- Ask a grownup to help you gently tap a pin or a big needle into the small end of an egg.
- Make a bigger hole in the big end of the egg.
- Hold the egg over a bowl as you blow through the small hole.
- When the shell is empty, wash it and use the insides of the egg for a meal.

Who Hatched?

Which of these creatures hatched from an egg?

Answer: They all do!

Paint Polkaroo
Draw a picture of Polkaroo.

EXPLORING

Let's Explore!

Take a look with Polkaroo
Through the door that's just for you.
What's beyond it? What's in store?
Fun and wonder. Let's explore!

Bees

Bzzzz! Bzzzz! The polkaroo bee buzzed happily through the field, enjoying the hot summer day. Life as a bee was wonderful! The flowers were even brighter and smelled twice as good so close up.

"Hey, c'mon," danced a fellow bee. "Don't dawdle. We must be busy, busy, busy all day long."

"Polkaroo!" buzzed Polkaroo and followed the other bee into the hive. What a busy place it was! Bees zipped here and there and everywhere. Some were storing flower nectar to make honey. Others were caring for the queen bee, and still others were watching over the young bees in the nursery.

Polkaroo's new-found friend was already zooming out of the hive again. Polkaroo was tired, but he followed the bee. "Mmmmmm," buzzed the other bee, "I smell jam." The two bees followed the scent until they arrived at an open

window and an open jar of fresh strawberry jam. They were just about to alight on the jar when Polkaroo noticed a shadow overhead. It was a fly swatter shadow!

"Polkaroo!" buzzed Polkaroo in warning, and away they zoomed....

Fame

"Bravo! Bravo!" shouted the audience, clapping with all their might. Polkaroo bowed once again. The spotlight beams centered upon him. The red, red roses in his arms were cool and fragrant and fresh. A pure gold medal, engraved with "Polka Champion of the World," hung heavily around his neck. Polkaroo, world-class dancer, was famous!

Finally, the curtain came down for the last time. Polkaroo danced off the stage to his dressing room. He sat before his mirror, wiping off his stage make-up with sticky cold cream. He listened to the laughter of the theater-goers as they clambered into cars and taxis. Soon the theater doors were locked, and all was quiet. Polkaroo was alone. He bent down to undo his shoes. "Polkaroo," he groaned. His feet hurt as never before....

Space

"Earth calling Commander Polkaroo on Starship Pluto. Our computers show that you can attempt a landing. Good luck, sir!"

"Polkaroo!" replied Commander Polkaroo, and with that he fastened his seat belt and pressed the "LAND" button. When the engines stopped humming, Polkaroo looked through the porthole. He couldn't see any life forms, but the ground outside was glowing with a mysterious green light. Polkaroo knew there was no time to waste. It was time to explore.

Stepping outside, he noticed a path of yellow and purple polka dots shining amidst green rocks and dust. "Polkaroo!" he exclaimed.

"Polkaroo!" The sound echoed from the rocks. As if a magic password, it brought the polka dots to life. Slowly each round circle opened, and out popped some strange-looking creatures. They were tall and green and covered in polka dots. "Polkaroo!" they shouted back to Polkaroo....

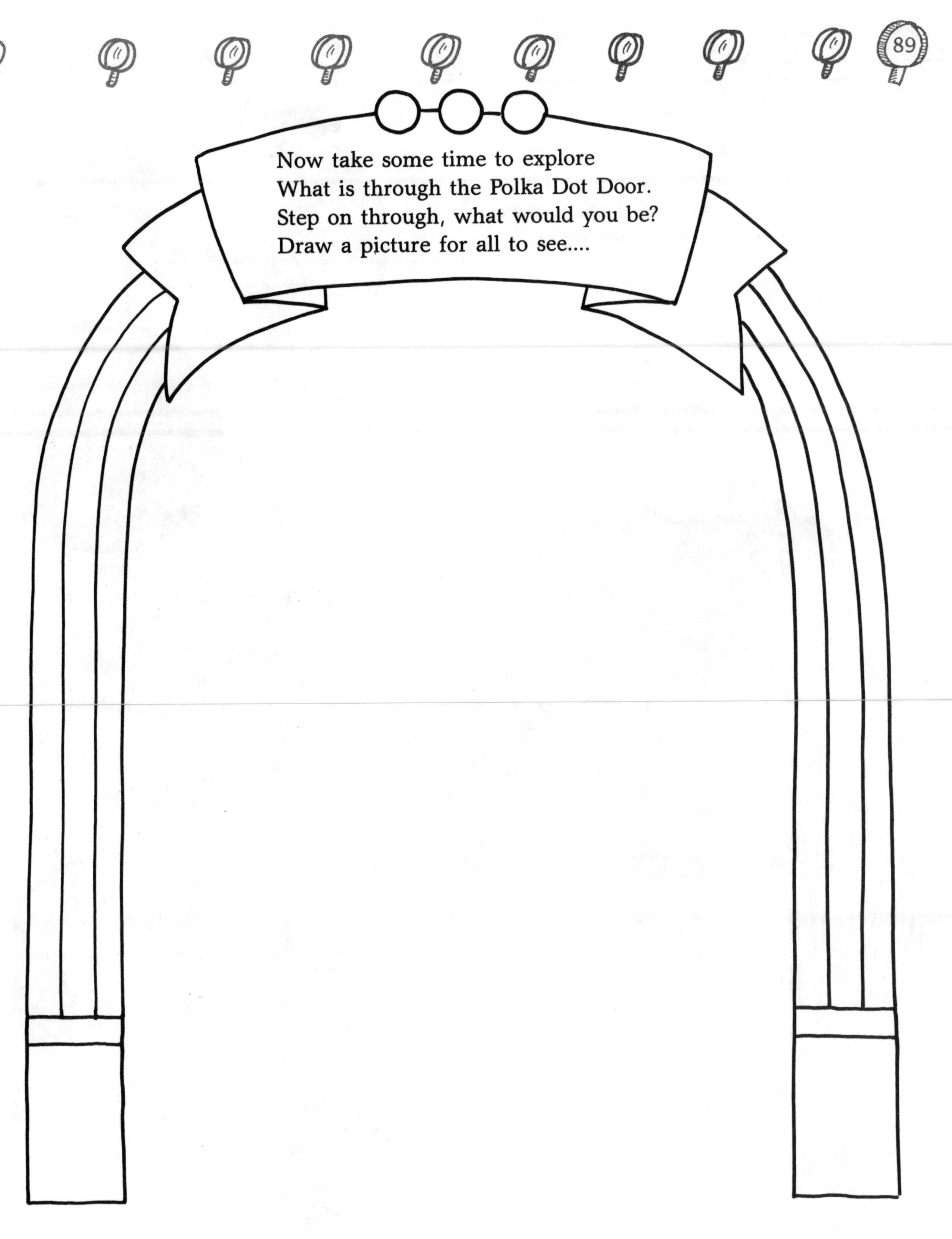
Now take some time to explore
What is through the Polka Dot Door.
Step on through, what would you be?
Draw a picture for all to see....

I Spy

The toys are hiking in the woods. They are using paper tubes to take a close-up look at what's around them. Can you find what each of them is looking at in the picture?

Hiking Tips

- When you go hiking, be sure to invite a grownup to come along.
- Be sure to tell someone where you are going and when you plan to be home.
- Take along a paper tube to help you look closely at the various plants and animals.
- Sit down and shut your eyes. What do you hear?
- Take along a snack of raisins, nuts and cereal and don't leave any waste behind. Never eat anything growing in the woods without asking a grownup.
- Always be prepared for a change in the weather; take along a sweater, a jacket or a raincoat. And don't forget your hat.
- As you walk along, see how many animals, trees and flowers you can name.

Answer: Marigold, a flower. Bear, a deer print. Humpty, an owl. Dumpty, a frog.

Let's All Go Exploring!

by Susan Murgatroyd

Let's all go exploring!
It's never boring —
Things to see, things to do,
New friends to greet,
New places to eat,
Let's all go exploring!

Wonder what's around the corner,
Wonder what's down the street.
Look here and there,
Look far and near,
Wonder who you will meet.

See something new and different,
Wonder what it's all about.
Look up and over,
Look down and under,
Explore and find out.

Let's all go exploring!
It's never boring —
Things to see, things to do,
New friends to meet,
New places to eat,
Let's all go exploring!

Color the Shapes

Color all the circles and triangles you can find in picture.

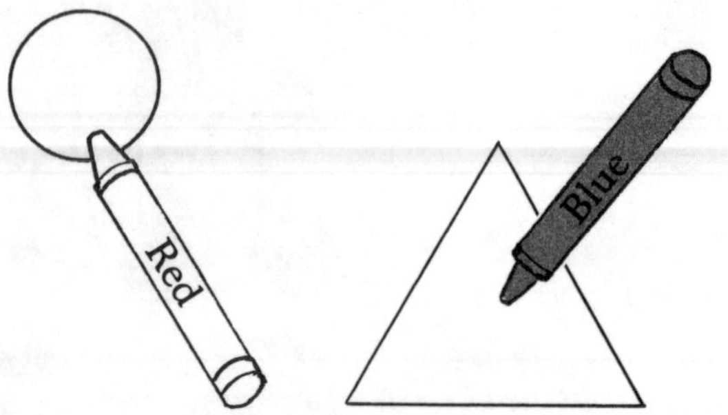

Help Polkaroo

Polkaroo has been exploring the library, but now he's lost. To find his way out, he must follow the numbers from 1 to 8. Help him find the exit. Can you spot the books below along the way?

TVO Presents
TODAY'S SPECIAL
EASY EN-CY-CLO-PEDIA
BOOKS
BOOKS FOR FUN!
2
3
4
SCIENCE IS SUPER
6
5
in
out
THIS WEEK
EXIT
8

Find the Secret Word

Look carefully at this picture to find eight hidden letters. They spell a secret word. Once you've found the letters, try to figure out the secret word.
Then fill in Polkaroo's speech balloon.

Bye!

See you soon on The Polka Dot Door!

Answer: Polkaroo!